Geometry Three

BY DAVID FLETCHER AND
JOSEPH IBBOTSON

General Editor: Professor F. W. LAND
University of Hull

HOLMES McDOUGALL LTD.,
30 ROYAL TERRACE,
EDINBURGH.

7157   0764 - 7

FOREWORD

Geometry One, Geometry Two and Geometry Three

There are plenty of ideas in 'Geometry Three' for individual activities and it needs to be used together with coloured paper, rulers, scissors, plastic shapes and other material which the children can manipulate for themselves.

This book explores the properties of triangles, squares and circles; other shapes will be dealt with in the other two books in the series. The emphasis is on planned and guided activity which is designed to give pupils an intuitive understanding of simple geometric concepts and spatial relationships by illustrations, examples and exercises which are expressed in the appropriate vocabulary of elementary geometry so that activity and the use of the correct language develop together.

The range of activities, which is well suited to the beginner, includes paper cutting and folding, clearly directed activities with rulers, pencils and scissors—making shapes with drinking straws, pipe cleaners and paste. It also makes use of Tangram pieces and patterns made with coloured gummed paper. Topics explored include exploration of area and perimeter; radius, diameter and circumference of circles; angles and symmetry.

The book should, of course, be used in conjunction with the many other activities in the school which involve number work and other intellectual ideas.

I am delighted with the production of the book, its very attractiveness should help children to get interested in its contents.

F. W. Land.
The University of Hull.

Geometry Three

CONTENTS

INTRODUCTION

The child who has enjoyed making directed investigations as suggested in 'Geometry One' and 'Geometry Two' will have sufficient experience on which to build a more organised understanding of spatial relationships.

Experience has repeatedly shown that there is no ceiling to the ability of young children to use and observe mathematical forms, provided there is a stimulating and exciting environment in which the child is allowed to satisfy his natural urge to make discoveries.

The contents of 'Geometry Three' are planned so as to revise the more important geometrical concepts covered in the first two books before developing them further.

In this book the topics are considerably widened in order to offer a challenge to the brightest child. At the same time there is such a wide range of material offered that less able children will find much that they can understand and build on.

SETS OF SHAPES USING PUNCHED CARDS

In selecting the shapes studied we can make those shown on the opposite page the universal set (set U).
This universal set is made up of a number of sub sets.

Triangles
    a. equilateral b. acute angled isosceles
    c. right angled isosceles d. obtuse angled
    isosceles e. right angled scalene f. scalene.

Quadrilaterals
    g. square h. rhombus i. rectangle
    j. parallelogram k. scalene quadrilateral
    l. scalene trapezium m. right angled
    trapezium n. isosceles trapezium o. deltoid

Polygons
    p. regular pentagon q. and r. equiangular
    pentagons s. equilateral pentagon
    t. irregular pentagon u. regular hexagon v.
    w. and x. equiangular hexagons y. equilateral
    hexagon z. irregular hexagon aa. regular
    octagon bb. and cc. equiangular octagons
    dd. irregular octagon.

These sub sets can be identified by using a punched card system and can be said to be:

Key
1. Shapes with exactly 3 sides.
2. Shapes with exactly 4 sides.
3. Shapes with more than 4 sides.
4. Shapes with all angles equal. Equiangular.
5. Shapes with all sides of equal length. Equilateral.
6. Shapes with any two sides parallel.
7. Shapes with at least one right angle.
8. Shapes with at least 5 right angles.
9. Shapes which are regular.
10. Shapes whose vertices always lie on the circumference of a circle.
11. Shapes which have bi-lateral symmetry.
12. Shapes which have rotational symmetry about a point.

PREPARING THE PUNCHED CARDS

Take 30 post cards, cut off one corner as shown and punch 12 holes a centimetre apart and a centimetre from one edge.
This can be done as a class exercise, each member preparing one or more cards.

On each card draw one shape from the universal set and write its name.

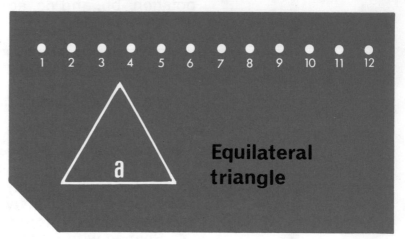

Number the punched holes from 1 to 12.

Now consult the key.

The equilateral triangle	Key number
has exactly 3 sides	1
has all angles equal	4
has sides of equal length	5
is regular	9
has vertices which always lie on the circumference of a circle	10
has bi-lateral symmetry	11
has rotational symmetry about a point...........	12

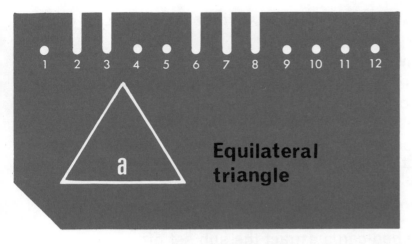

Equilateral triangle

The holes numbered 1, 4, 5, 9, 10, 11, and 12 are therefore left intact and the remaining holes cut away as shown. The card for the equilateral triangle will now look like this.

Repeat this with all the shapes in the universal set. Consult the key and leave the punched hole intact when the shape has the particular property represented by that hole.

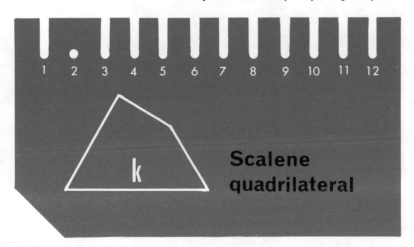

Scalene quadrilateral

Here is the card of the scalene quadrilateral.
It has only one property—a shape with exactly 4 sides—number 2 on the key.
Number 2 hole is therefore left intact and all the others cut away.

Using the punched cards

Assemble the cards, in any order, so that the cut-off corners come together. It is now possible to select sub sets.

Example

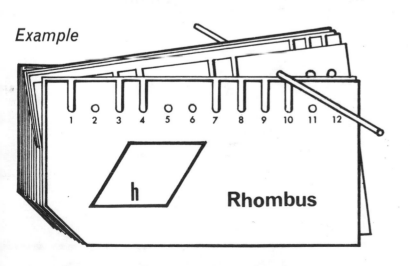

Rhombus

To select the sub set of all shapes whose vertices always lie on the circumference of a circle.
This is number 10 on the key.
Push a knitting needle through hole number 10 and shake out the cards.
Those remaining on the knitting needle make up the sub set of shapes whose vertices always lie on the circumference of a circle.
Record the members of this sub set.

3

To select the sub set of shapes which have all sides of equal length and are regular.

These are shown on the key as No. 5 and No. 9.

First select the cards representing the sub set of shapes which have all sides of equal length by inserting the knitting needle in hole No. 5 and shaking out the cards.

Assemble these cards and insert the knitting needle in hole No. 9 to extract the cards representing the sub set of shapes which are regular.

Record your findings.

Using the punched cards extract the sub set of:

a. Shapes which are equiangular.

b. Shapes with at least one right-angle.

c. Shapes which have bi-lateral symmetry.

d. Shapes which have exactly 3 sides and which are regular.

e. Shapes which have any two sides parallel and at least one right-angle.

f. Shapes whose vertices always lie on the circumference of a circle and which have rotational symmetry.

g. Shapes which have 5 right angles.
(How would you describe this set?)

h. Shapes with more than 4 sides and which are equinagular.

i Shapes which have exactly 4 sides and are equilateral.

j. Shapes which are equiangular and equilateral.

k. Shapes which are regular, have bi-lateral symmetry and have more than 4 sides.

l. Shapes which are equiangular, have rotational symmetry about a point and whose vertices always lie on the circumference of a circle.

Record your answers.

ORGANISING YOUR KNOWLEDGE OF ANGLES

So that mathematicians in different parts of the world can share a common understanding and a common language it is necessary to standardise the terminology and diagrammatic symbols.

Naming Angles
Here are some ways of naming an angle.

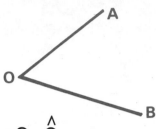

$\angle O.$ $\hat{O}.$

Angle AOB.

$\hat{AOB}.$ $\angle AOB.$

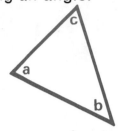

Angle a

$\hat{a}$

$\angle a.$

Angle $a + b + c = 180°$

$\hat{a} + \hat{b} + \hat{c} = 180°$

$\angle a + \angle b + \angle c = 180°$

Naming equal angles
The angles in regular shapes are all equal and are named with the same letter with a numeral added.

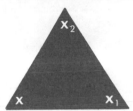
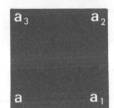

The right angle Abbreviation rt $\angle$ Sign ∟

Parallel lines
Arrows are used to indicate that lines are parallel.

Lines of equal length
Thin lines are used to mark lines of equal length.

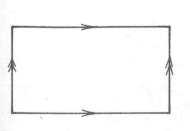
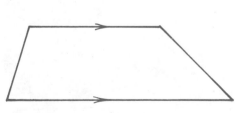
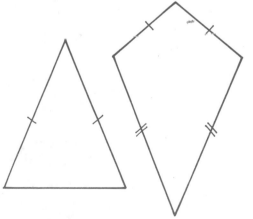

When two parallel lines are intersected by a third line, alternate angles are obtained, the two angles in each case being equal.

Use two rulers side by side to draw two parallel lines. Draw a third line intersecting them.

Number the angles as shown and cut them out. You will now have eight angles.

By placing them one on top of the other find out which angles are congruent.

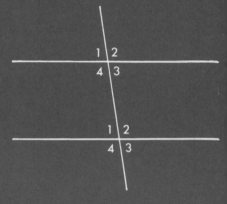

You should now be able to calculate the seven remaining angles below.

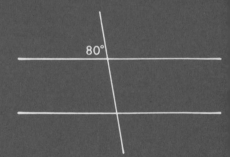

When two parallel lines are intersected by a third line corresponding angles are made.

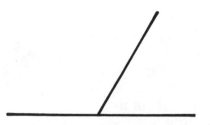

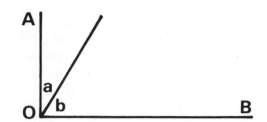

A straight line angle measures 180°. When two adjacent (side by side) angles together measure 180° the angles are called supplementary angles. Each angle is said to supplement the other.

Since AOB is a right angle the angles a and b together measure 90°. When two adjacent angles together measure 90° they are called complementary angles. Each angle is the complement of the other.

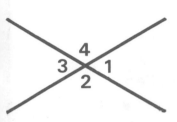

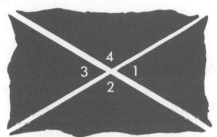

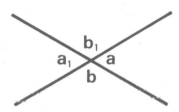

Four angles are obtained when two straight lines intersect.

On a sheet of plain paper draw two intersecting lines. Number the angles 1, 2, 3, 4 and cut them out.
By placing these angles on top of one another find out which are congruent (equal).

The angles opposite each other are called vertically opposite angles.

Shapes made with straight lines have angles. If the shape is regular the angles and the sides will be equal.

Irregular shapes.

Regular shapes.

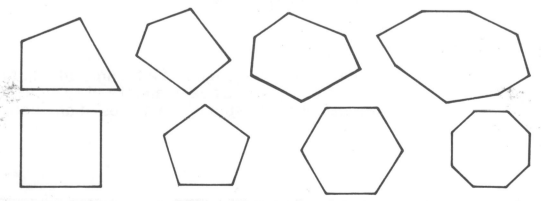

Angles in the Triangle

Draw and cut out 3 different scalene triangles.

Name the angles a, b and c. From a point in the triangle draw three lines, one to the middle of each side dividing the triangle into three regions.

Cut or tear along the lines and then place the angles together along a straight line.

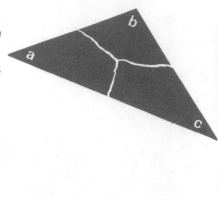

The angles of any triangle placed together are equal to half a revolution or 2 rt. angles or 180°.

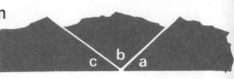

Angles in a quadrilateral

Draw and cut out 3 different irregular quadrilaterals.
Name the angles a b c and d.
Divide the quadrilateral into
4 parts as shown.
Place the angles together at a point.

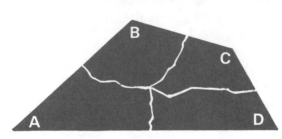

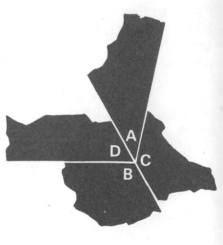

The 4 angles of a quadrilateral together are equal to one revolution or 4 rt. angles or 360°.

The fact that the angles of a triangle add up to 2 rt. angles and the angles of a quadrilateral add up to 4 rt. angles can be used to calculate the sum of the angles of any polygon.

Always think of an angle as a fraction of a circle.
This is still possible even when the arms of the angle make the side of a shape.
A small circle has been drawn with the vertex of each angle as centre.
Study these shapes and estimate each angle.
What do you notice about the sum of the angles of each triangle? *measure*
What do you notice about the sum of the angles of each quadrilateral? *measure*

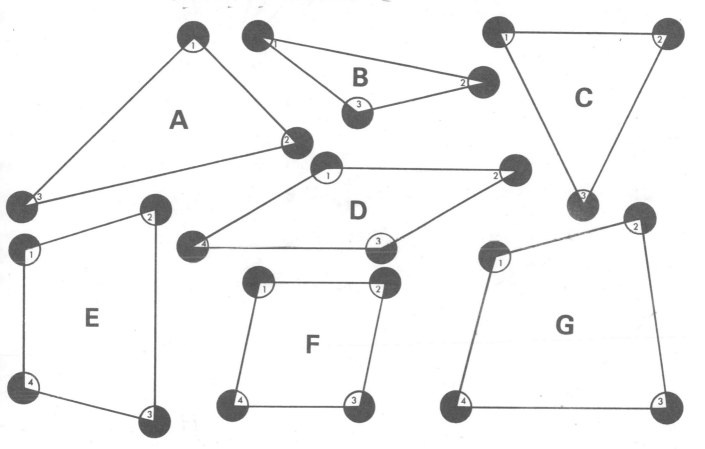

An angle is a fraction of a circle expressed in 360th's.

Example

A.1. This angle (shown white) is $\frac{1}{4}$ of the full circle.
$\frac{1}{4} = \frac{90}{360}$ so the angle is 90°.

B.1. This angle is about $\frac{1}{3}$ of a quarter turn or $\frac{1}{12}$ of the circle.
$\frac{1}{12} = \frac{30}{360}$ so angle B.1 is approximately 30°.

Estimate the remaining angles. Check whether they add up to 180° in the case of a triangle or 360° in the case of a quadrilateral.

THE PROTRACTOR

Since an angle can turn either from the left or from the right, the protractor must be numbered to measure in two directions. The examples given are for the semi-circular protractor but apply equally well to the circular protractor.

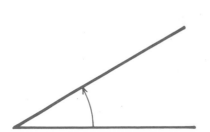

This angle turns from the right.

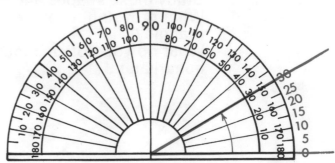

To measure it we must count from the right beginning 0, 5, 10, 15, ...

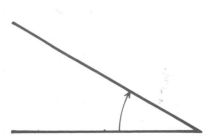

This angle turns from the left.

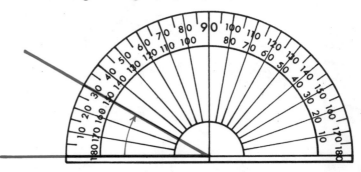

To measure it we must count from the left beginning 0, 5, 10, 15, ...

It is a great help when measuring an angle to begin counting from 0 upwards until the line showing the amount of turn is reached.

Measure each of the sixteen angles in this shape.

How can you check some of your results?

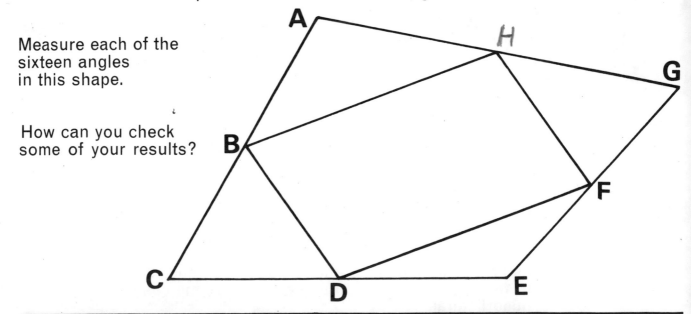

USING THE PROTRACTOR TO MAKE ANGLES

These three triangles have been drawn using a protractor.

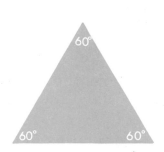

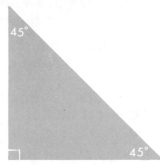

Draw a line 10 cm long.

Place the protractor over one end of the line as shown and mark the position of the angle required.
Remove the protractor and join up the mark to the end of the line to complete the angle.

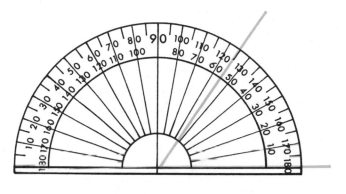

Repeat this by placing the protractor at the other end of the line.

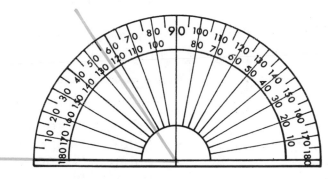

Extend both lines to complete the triangle.

In the same way construct the three triangles shown above.

USING A PROTRACTOR

Protractors are usually made from a transparent plastic material so that, when placed over the angle to be measured, the arms of the angle can be seen through the plastic.

Protractors can be obtained which are either circular and are marked in 360 divisions, or semi-circular which show 180 divisions.
Although the semi-circular protractor is sufficient to measure any angle, the circular protractor is perhaps the easiest to understand and use.

Here are some wheels. Count the number of spokes in each wheel.

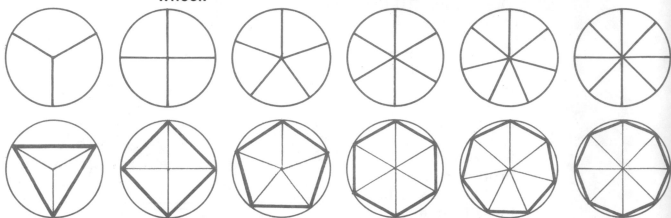

Discuss with your teacher how the 360 divisions or degrees in a circle would be partitioned by the spokes.
If one spoke is placed at the O in a circular protractor can you find to which numbers the other spokes would point?

Record your findings by completing this table

Equilateral
  triangle (3 spokes) 0° 120° 240° 360°
Square   (4 spokes) 0° 90° 180° 270° 360°
Pentagon (5 spokes) 0° 72° —— —— —— ——
Hexagon (6 spokes) 0° 60° —— —— —— —— ——
Heptagon (7 spokes) 0° —— —— —— —— —— —— ——
Octagon (8 spokes) 0° —— —— —— —— —— —— —— ——

Use this information to draw some regular shapes.

Here is an example
Place a circular protractor on the paper and mark off the points as shown for a Pentagon.

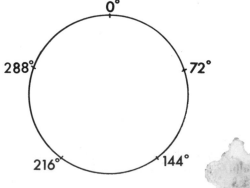

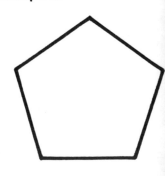

MEASURING ANGLES

The following triangles are all parts of regular polygons. The angle marked C would be placed at the centre of the polygon.
Measure this angle with your protractor and say how many of these triangles would be required to complete the polygon.
Can you calculate what the other two angles of each triangle would be? Check your answer by measuring with your protractor.

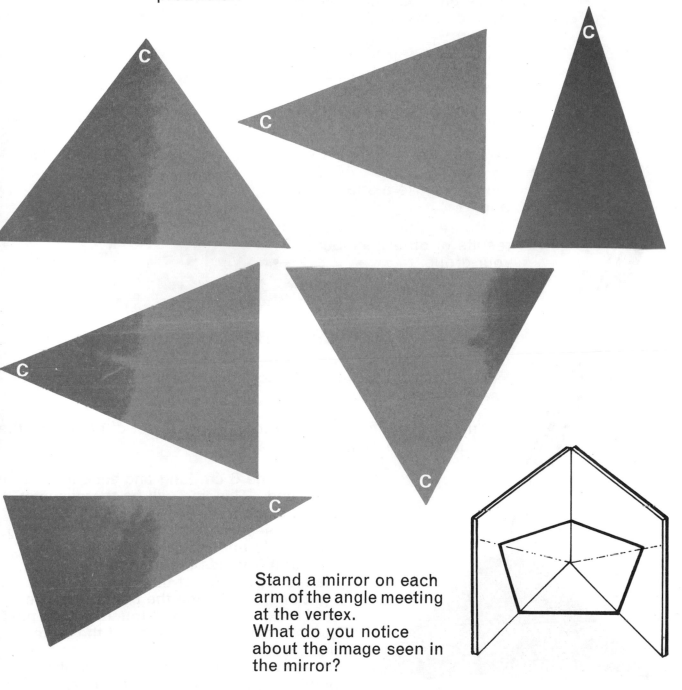

Stand a mirror on each arm of the angle meeting at the vertex.
What do you notice about the image seen in the mirror?

ANGLES IN A SEMI-CIRCLE

Take a circle shape. A diameter of 6 cm is a convenient size. Fold the centre along a diameter and cut to make two semi-circles.

Mark any point on the circumference of each semi-circle and join this point to each end of the diameter as shown.

Name the angles formed at the circumference A and B.
Cut out the triangles.
Put angle A over angle B.
What do you notice?

Arrange the two angles side by side.
Do they make a straight line angle?

Compare your results with the results of other members of your group.

What can you say about every angle made in this way in a semi-circle?

You can use this knowledge to help plot a set of points on the circumference of a circle.

Draw a line 6 cm long and stick a pin at each end. This line will be the diameter of the circle.
Take a piece of card or stiff paper with a right angle and place it between the pins so that it touches them both.
Mark the position of the vertex of the right angle. Change the position of the card making sure that it touches both pins and mark the new position of the vertex of the right angle.
Repeat this until you have sufficient points to join up to make a curve.

ANGLES

On page 8 it was shown that the four angles of any quadrilateral add up to 360°. When any quadrilateral, regular or irregular, is reproduced several times the pieces can be used to form a mosaic or tessellation.

Draw any irregular quadrilateral and make twelve identical copies on thin card.

Mark the angles on each quadrilateral A B C D and fit the quadrilaterals to make a pattern.

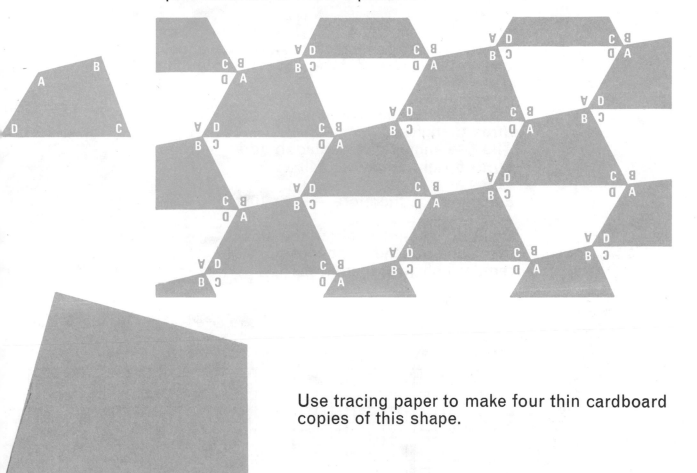

Use tracing paper to make four thin cardboard copies of this shape.

Fit them together to make a square.

Now make a square with a hole in the centre.

Arrange the four pieces to form a tile which can be repeated to cover a surface.

THE ANGLES OF REGULAR POLYGONS

Here are 8 regular polygons. Each polygon is regular because in each case all the sides are equal and all the angles are equal.

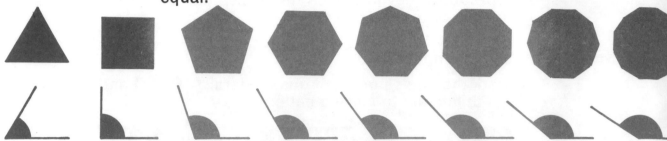

Since the angles in each polygon are equal it is possible to calculate the size of the angle of any regular polygon.

The regular pentagon has five sides and can be divided into three triangles.
The five angles of a pentagon add up to 6 right angles or 540°.

Each angle is therefore $\dfrac{540°}{5}$ or 108°.

What do you notice about the size of the angle as the number of sides of regular polygons increases?

Example—The regular pentagon.

Draw a graph to show the relationship between the number of sides of a regular polygon and the size of the interior angle.

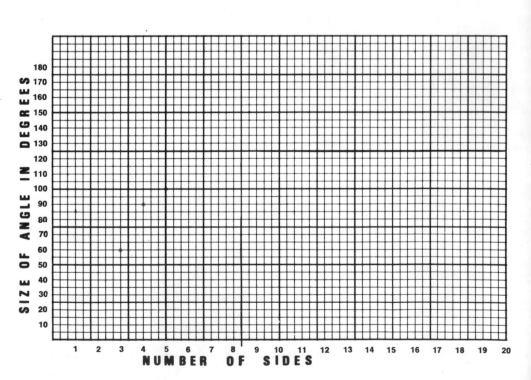

ANGLES AND THE ISOSCELES TRIANGLE

An isosceles triangle has two equal sides.
On a 7 cm base construct three triangles each of a different height.

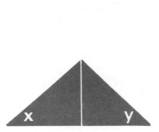  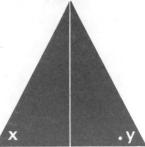

Cut out each triangle and fold along the line of symmetry.

What do you notice about the angles x and y?

When one angle in an isosceles triangle is named it is possible to name the other two. Why?

Make rough sketches of these triangles and state the sizes of all three angles.

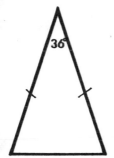 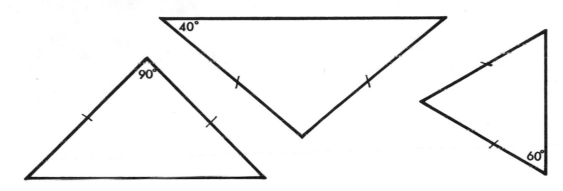

Trace or make rough sketches of these shapes and name all the angles.

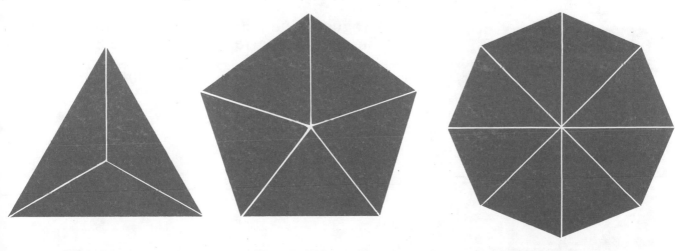

THE EXTERIOR ANGLES OF REGULAR POLYGONS

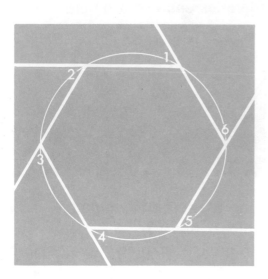

Take a square of coloured paper, find the centre by drawing in the diagonals and draw a circle of radius ~~5~~ cm. *4cm*

Using the same radius mark off the six equal sides of a regular hexagon.

Extend each side and number the angles as shown here.

Cut out the 6 angles and place them on top of one another.

What do you notice?

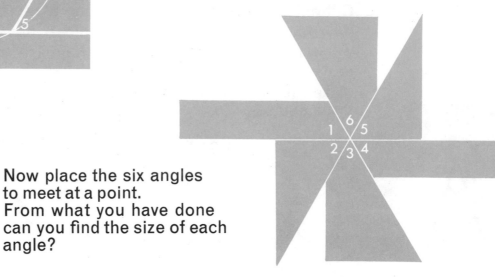

Now place the six angles to meet at a point.

From what you have done can you find the size of each angle?

To find the exterior and interior angles of a regular shape

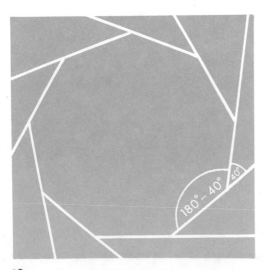

A regular nine sided shape (nonagon).

The nine exterior angles add up to 360° so each

exterior angle will be $\frac{360°}{9} = 40°$.

The interior angle will be
$180° - 40° = 140°$.

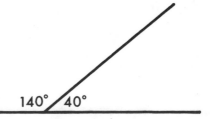

ANGLES AND POLYGONS

Trace or make rough sketches of the regular shapes below and calculate the size of all the angles.

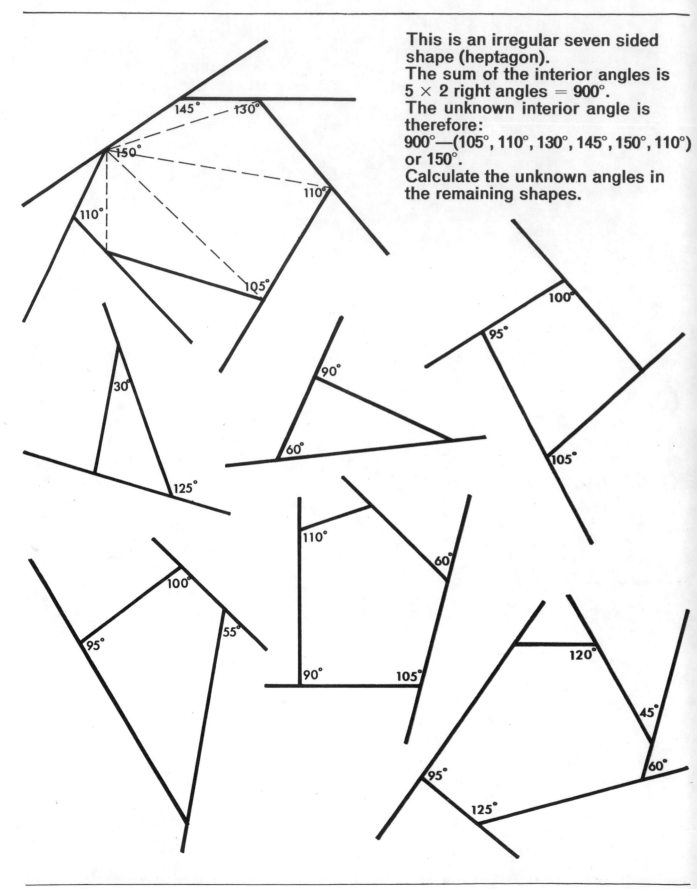

This is an irregular seven sided shape (heptagon).
The sum of the interior angles is 5 × 2 right angles = 900°.
The unknown interior angle is therefore:
900°—(105°, 110°, 130°, 145°, 150°, 110°) or 150°.
Calculate the unknown angles in the remaining shapes.

AREA

Area is the measurement of a surface and is named in square units. The units may be the square millimetre, the square centimetre, the square metre or the square kilometre.

A square millimetre may be written either as sq. mm or mm^2.
If you see cm^2 or sq. cm you read this as square centimetre.
When you see km^2 you will say square kilometre.

Area is best understood by finding how many squares are required to cover a particular surface. Draw and cut out the following shape into its seven pieces.

1 square
centimetre

100 square
millimetres.

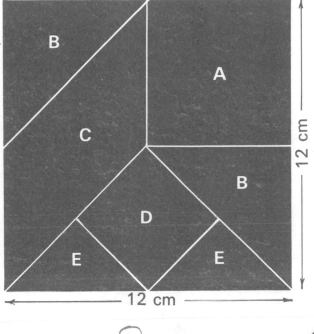

How many of one centimetre squares are needed to cover the large square A?

By placing the two large triangles B on the square A find the area of each triangle.

In the same way place the two small triangles E on a large triangle B and so find the area of each small triangle.

How can you find the area of the small square D and the parallelogram C?

Use the pieces to make the following shapes and state the area of each.

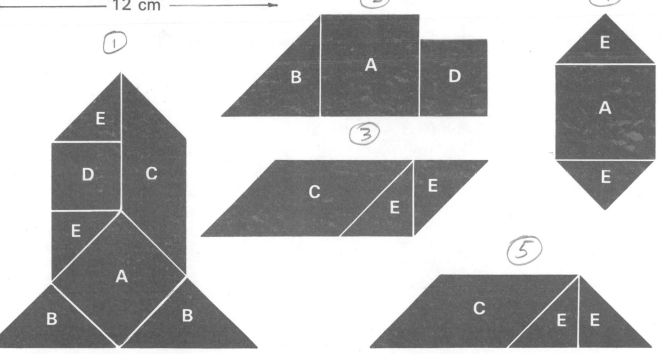

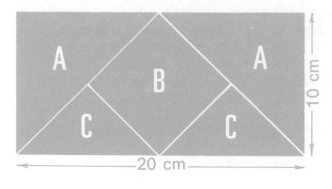

On cardboard or squared paper copy this diagram and cut out five pieces.
Use squared paper to record the way in which the pieces are rearranged to form:

a. a square.
b. a parallelogram.
c. a trapezium.
d. a triangle.

Make up some outline shapes for your partner to construct. All five pieces must be used.

Area is to do with surface and is measured in square units.

Discuss with your teacher how the following would be measured.

(a) lawns.   (c) carpets.   (e) lakes.   (g) continents.
(b) concrete.   (d) fields.   (f) counties.   (h) seas.

Present the following information as a block graph.

Area of the six largest lakes in the world (to the nearest 100 km²)

Superior (U.S.A.-Canada)	82,400 km²
Victoria (Africa)	69,400 km²
Aral (U.S.S.R.)	63,700 km²
Huron (U.S.A.-Canada)	59,600 km²
Michigan (U.S.A.)	58,000 km²
Chad (Africa)	51,800 km²

Cut out in cardboard a square metre.
Use this to find the approximate area of

    (a) the desk top.
    (b) the table top.
    (c) the blackboard.
    (d) a ruler.
    (e the classroom door.

AREA Look at the following diagrams which you studied in 'Geometry Two' and discuss with your teacher how they show that the area of any triangle is found by halving the product of the vertical height and the base.

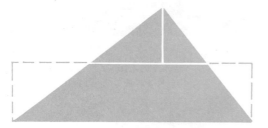

The area of a triangle is half the area of a rectangle drawn on the same base and with the same vertical height.

$$\frac{\text{Height} \times \text{base}}{2}$$

The following triangles each have the same area. Can you explain why?

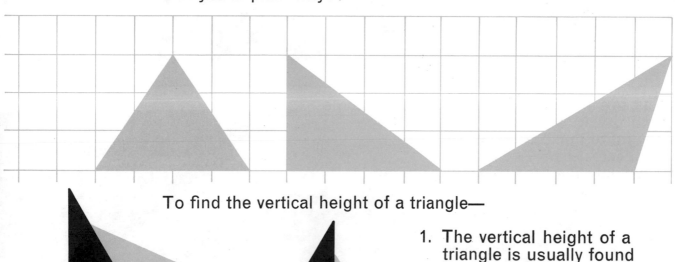

To find the vertical height of a triangle—

1. The vertical height of a triangle is usually found with the aid of a set square.

2. When it is possible to cut out the triangle the vertical height can be found by folding.

Use your ruler to find the dimensions of these triangles to the nearest half – centimetre and calculate their area in sq. cm.

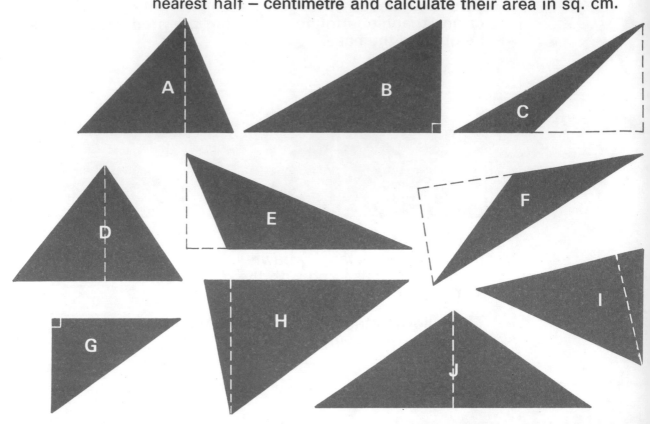

Cut out a copy of this right angled triangle and use it to find the vertical height of these triangles to the nearest half – centimetre. Calculate the area of each in sq. cm.

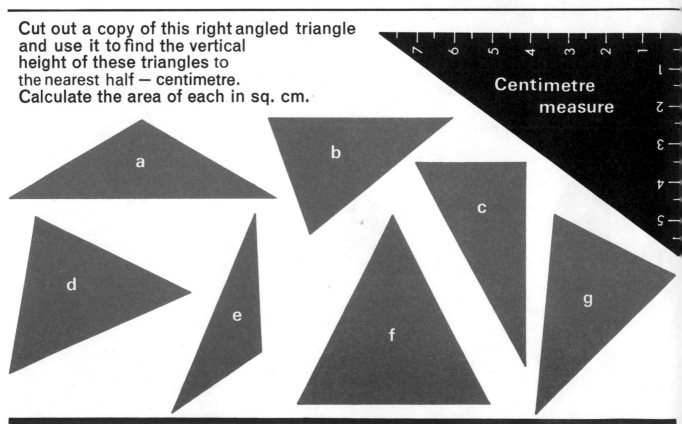

Make and complete the following tables.

Base of Triangle	Perpendi-cular Ht.	Area
30 mm	40 mm	mm²
20 mm	50 mm	mm²
70 mm	60 mm	mm²
10 mm	90 mm	mm²
150 mm	120 mm	mm²
150 mm	150 mm	mm²

Base of Triangle	Perpendi-cular Ht.	Area
30 mm		210 mm²
	60 mm	420 mm²
25 mm	35 mm	mm²
	120 mm	540 mm²
	100 mm	1100 mm²
150 mm		1200 mm²

Construct triangles with the details given in this table.
Measure the perpendicular height and calculate the area of each triangle.

Base of Triangle	Side	Side
30 mm	40 mm	50 mm
60 mm	50 mm	50 mm
70 mm	40 mm	60 mm
100 mm	90 mm	45 mm
90 mm	55 mm	75 mm
70 mm	40 mm	80 mm

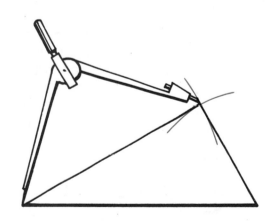

First draw the base.
From each end draw an
arc with radius the length
of the required side.
Join the intersection of the
arcs to the ends of the base.

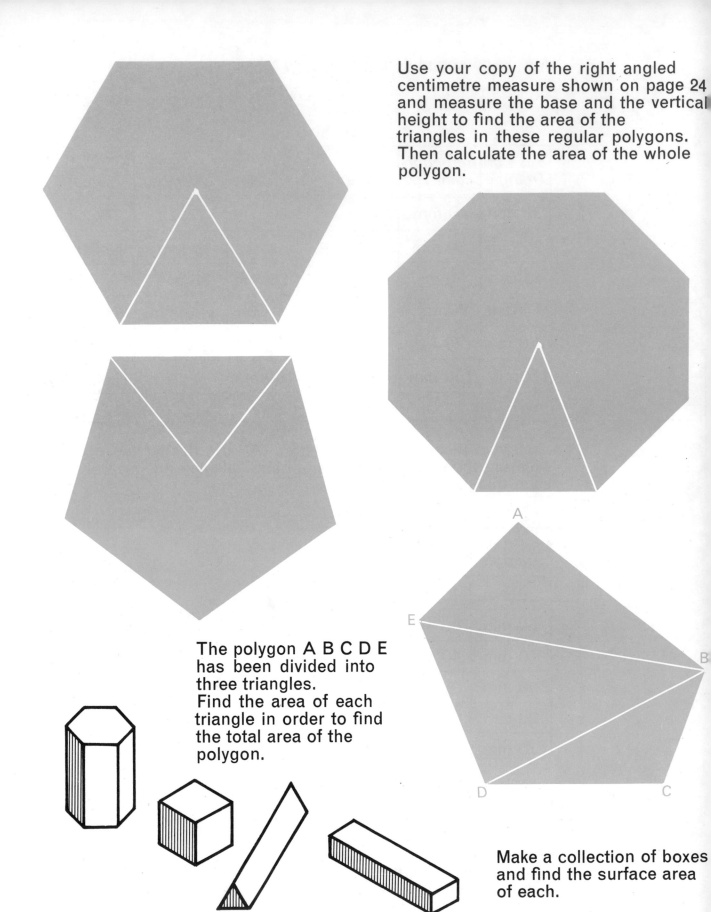

Use your copy of the right angled centimetre measure shown on page 24 and measure the base and the vertical height to find the area of the triangles in these regular polygons. Then calculate the area of the whole polygon.

The polygon A B C D E has been divided into three triangles.
Find the area of each triangle in order to find the total area of the polygon.

Make a collection of boxes and find the surface area of each.

THE AREA OF A PARALLELOGRAM

When the idea of area is understood you will want to explore as many ways as possible of finding the area of a shape to decide for yourself which method is the most convenient.

Here are three ways to find the area of a parallelogram using a cardboard set square marked in centimetres.

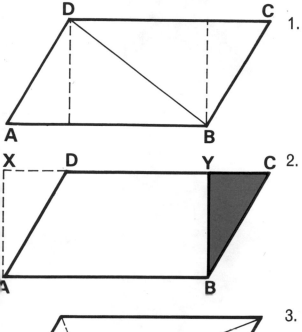

1. Divide the parallelogram into two equal triangles by drawing the shorter of the two diagonals BD.
   Find the vertical height of each triangle and calculate the area of the parallelogram. Is it necessary to calculate the area of both triangles?

2. If that part of the parallelogram which is shown coloured were moved to the position outlined by the dotted lines the parallelogram would be rearranged as a rectangle on the same base and with the same height as the parallelogram
   The parallelogram has the same area as the rectangle BYXA.

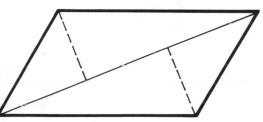

3. The parallelogram has been partitioned into two equal triangles by drawing the long diagonal.
   Find the area of each triangle by measuring the vertical height and multiplying it by half the base (in this case the diagonal of the parallelogram).

Find the area of these shapes in square centimetres.

Copy these shapes using tracing paper and find the area of each in square centimetres.

THE AREA OF A CIRCLE

The area of a circle has a special relationship with a square drawn on the radius of the circle.

Notice how the square increases in size as the radius of the circle increases.

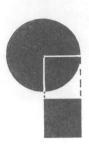 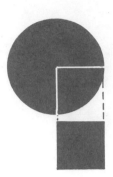 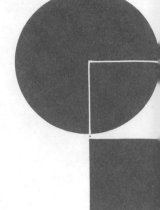

The side of each square measures the same as the radius of the corresponding circle, and as the area of the circle increases, so does the area of the square.

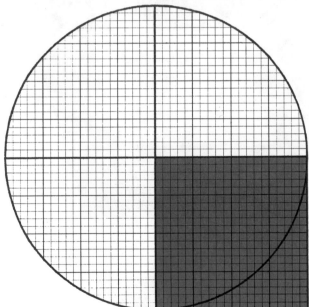

Using squared paper draw a circle and also draw a square the side of which is the radius of the circle.
The area of both the circle and the square can be found by counting the number of squares contained by each.
Work in a group of six, each member of the group to draw a different sized circle.
Count the number of squares and fill in the details in a table as shown.

Here is an example

How many times must the number of small squares in the coloured square be multiplied in order to equal the number of small squares in the full circle?

You should find the answer more than 3 but less than 4.

Name of member of group	Number of small squares in full circle	Number of small squares drawn on radius of circle
John	1257	400

To find the relationship between the area of a square and the area of a circle drawn inside the square when the diameter of the circle and the side of the square are the same length.

 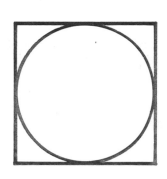 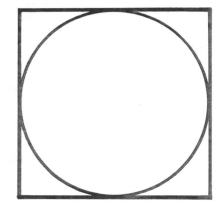

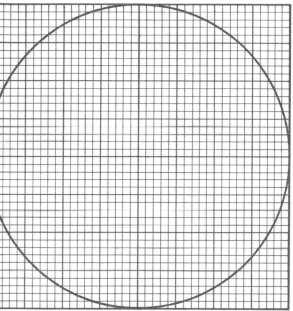

As the area of the square increases so does the area of the circle.

On graph paper draw a circle and a square as shown. By counting the numbers of small squares find the area of both the circle and the square.
Enter your findings in a table together with the findings of at least six of your friends.

Name of member of group	Area of Square	Area of Circle	Area of Circle / Area of Square

The approximate area of any circle can be found by multiplying the square drawn in the radius of the circle by $3\frac{1}{7}$ or 3·14.

The approximate area of any circle can also be found by taking $\frac{11}{14}$ of the area of the square enclosing the circle.

THE DIAMETER AND CIRCUMFERENCE OF A CIRCLE

A straight line across a circle passing through the centre is called a diameter.

The boundary line of a circle is called the circumference.

Examine these circles and notice how, as the diameter increases in length, so does the circumference.

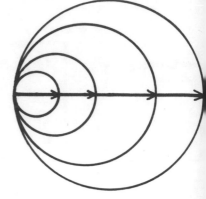

Two ways to find the circumference

Make a pin-prick through an overlapping strip of paper.

Make a pencil mark across an overlapping strip of paper.

Is the length of the diameter always contained in the length of the circumference the same number of times in any sized circle?

To find out, take a number of different sized circular jars or tins and make a series of paper strips each one equal in length to the circumference of one of the jars.

Paste down the strip of paper which is the length of the circumference of one of the jars and find out how many times you can mark off the length of the diameter.

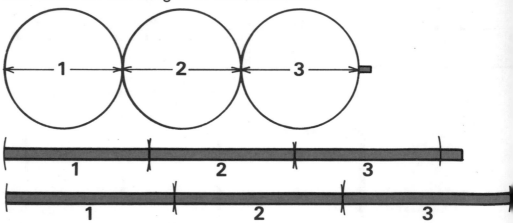

Repeat this for each size of tin until you have a number of paper strips marked off in diameters.

The circumference is slightly more than 3 times the diameter.

Can you write down a general rule from your experiments?

This straight line graph shows the relationship between the diameter and the circumference of a circle.

Use the graph to complete this table.

Give your answers to the nearest millimetre.

Diameter	Circum- ference
30 mm	
40 mm	
	188 mm
	141 mm
35 mm	
25 mm	
	157 mm
	204 mm
22 mm	
54 mm	
	60 mm
	120 mm

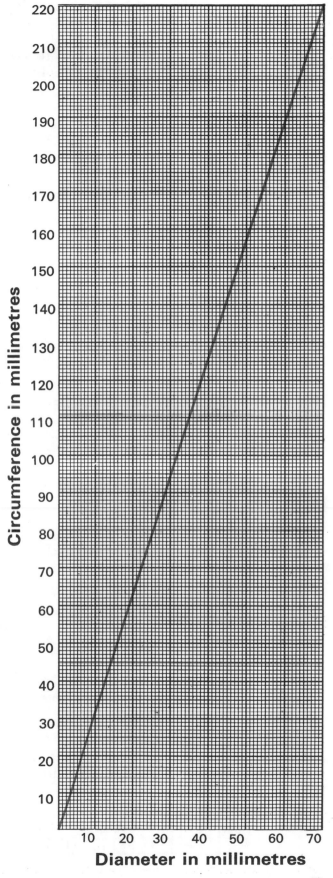

Circumference in millimetres

Diameter in millimetres

RECTANGLES WITH THE SAME AREA

The area of any rectangle can be found by multiplying the length by the breadth.

Use squared paper to cut out all the rectangles with an area of 60 squares.
60 × 1, 30 × 2, 20 × 3, 15 × 4
12 × 5, 10 × 6, 6 × 10, 5 × 12
4 × 15, 3 × 20, 2 × 30, 1 × 60

Paste the rectangles to make a graph as shown below and join the vertices of the rectangles to make a curve.

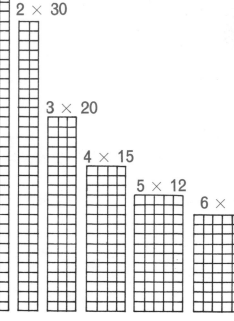

1 × 60

Each rectangle has an area of 60 squares. Which rectangle has the shortest perimeter?

2 × 30

3 × 20

4 × 15

5 × 12

6 × 10

10 × 6

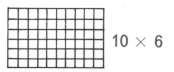

12 × 5

15 × 4

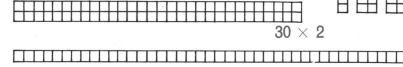

20 × 3

30 × 2

60 × 1

It is possible to obtain the same effect by drawing the rectangles on a large sheet of graph paper.

In the same way draw all the rectangles with an area of 120 squares beginning with 120 × 1 and ending with 1 × 120. Compare the curve joining the vertices of these rectangles with the one showing the rectangles making an area of 60 squares.

MAKING SOLIDS

Can you name the following shapes?

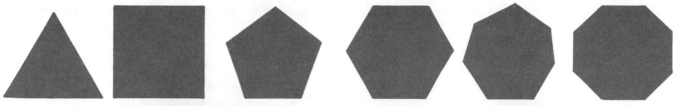

It has been known for centuries that only the square, the equilateral triangle and the pentagon can be used to make regular solids.

A regular solid is one where all the faces are the same shape and all the angles at each vertex are also the same.

There are five regular solids—frequently called Platonic solids after Plato.

1. This is the net of the cube—sometimes called the hexahedron because it has six faces.

Copy this diagram on to squared paper, carefully, putting in the numbers as shown.

Cut out the shape, fold and paste down the flaps to make a hexahedron.

Find out how many different ways you can add up the figures to make 194.

There are more ways than you think!

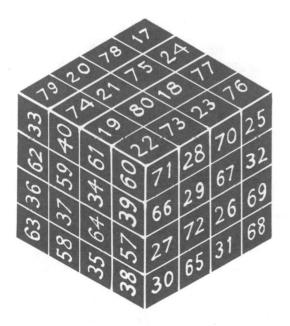

87	12	86	9
82	13	83	16
11	88	10	85
14	81	15	84

63	36	62	33	79	20	78	17	95	4	94	1
58	37	59	40	74	21	75	24	90	5	91	8
35	64	34	61	19	80	18	77	3	96	2	93
38	57	39	60	22	73	23	76	6	89	7	92

71	28	70	25
66	29	67	32
27	72	26	69
30	65	31	68

55	44	54	41
50	45	51	48
43	56	42	53
46	49	47	52

2. The Triangular Pyramid or Tetrahedron
Four equilateral triangles together form the net of a tetrahedron.

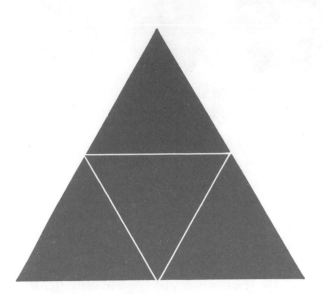

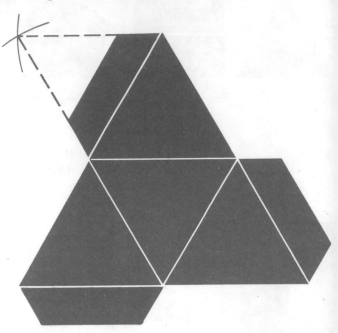

Draw an equilateral triangle on a 15 cm base and join the mid points of each side.

When adding flaps it is important to make them the correct shape. Flaps for this model should be parts of equilateral triangles as shown in the diagram above.

It is essential to score along the lines before creasing and pasting down the flaps.

The four triangles forming the net can be decorated before folding. Alternatively, the tetrahedron can be sprayed when finished.

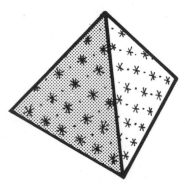

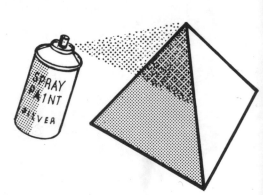

MAKING SOLIDS

3. The Octahedron

This is the net of the octahedron. There are several ways to draw this net. Below you will find one of them.

Can you find others?

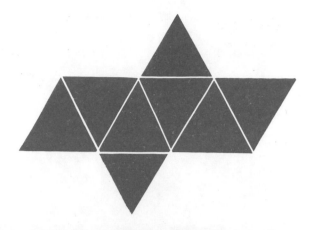

Make this pattern with semi-circles of 5 cm radius.

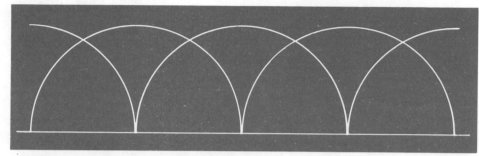

Draw in six equilateral triangles.

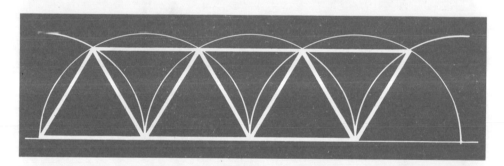

Add two more equilateral triangles as shown.

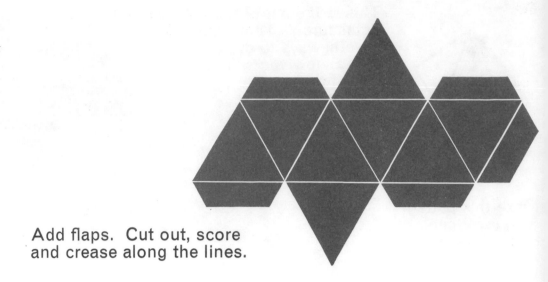

Add flaps. Cut out, score
and crease along the lines.

Fold and paste the flaps to
complete the octahedron.

MAKING SOLIDS

4. The Icosahedron

The net of this solid is made up of twenty equilateral triangles.

Draw six equal interlocking circles.

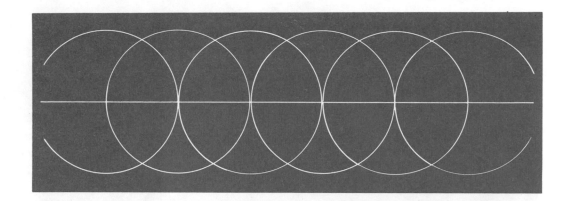

Add five more circles and join up to make twenty equilateral triangles.

Add flaps for pasting and cut out the shape.

Crease firmly and fold to make an icosahedron.

5. The Dodecahedron

This solid is made up of twelve pentagons and since it is a little difficult to make it will be explained in two parts.

The Pentagonal Tray

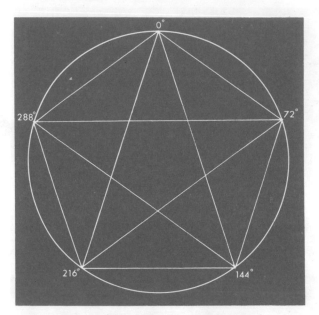

On a 15 cm diameter circle mark off the five points 0°, 72°, 144°, 216° and 288° as shown. Join up the points. What is the shape in the middle?

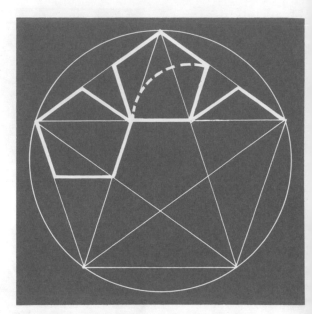

With the compasses set at the distance of one side of the middle pentagon, mark off from each corner and so obtain five more pentagons.

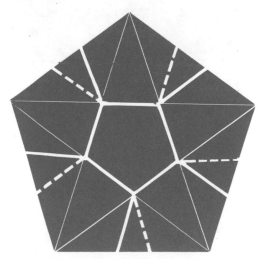

Cut along the dotted lines. The small triangles act as flaps for pasting.

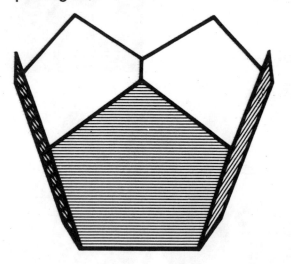

Crease firmly and fold to make a pentagonal tray. Is this a solid?

MAKING SOLIDS

The net of the dodecahedron.

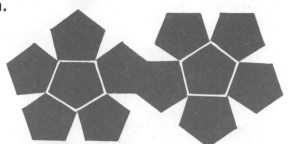

Two pentagonal trays placed together make a solid with twelve faces, each face being a pentagon.

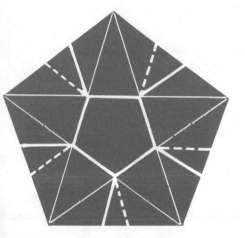

Cut out a pentagon and mark as for the pentagonal tray.

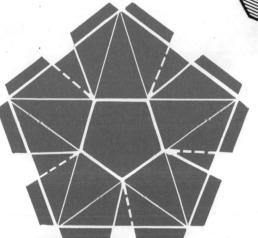

Cut out another and add flaps for pasting.

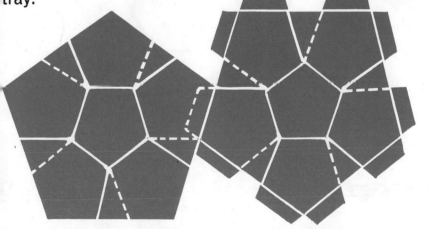

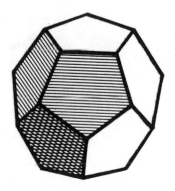

Join the two together, crease firmly and fold to make a dodecahedron.

In addition to the regular (or Platonic) solids there are a number of solids which can be made from a combination of regular polygons.

In the diagrams below the necessary flaps are shown coloure

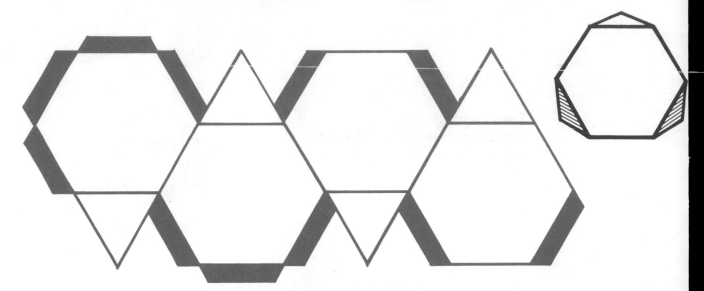

This is a truncated tetrahedron.

Truncate means, "to cut the top or the end from".

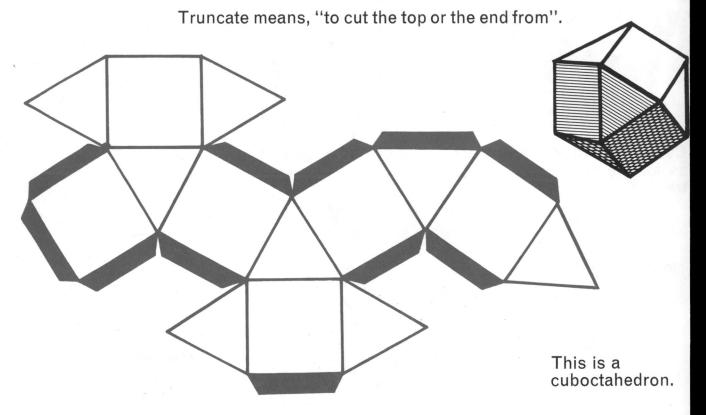

This is a cuboctahedron.

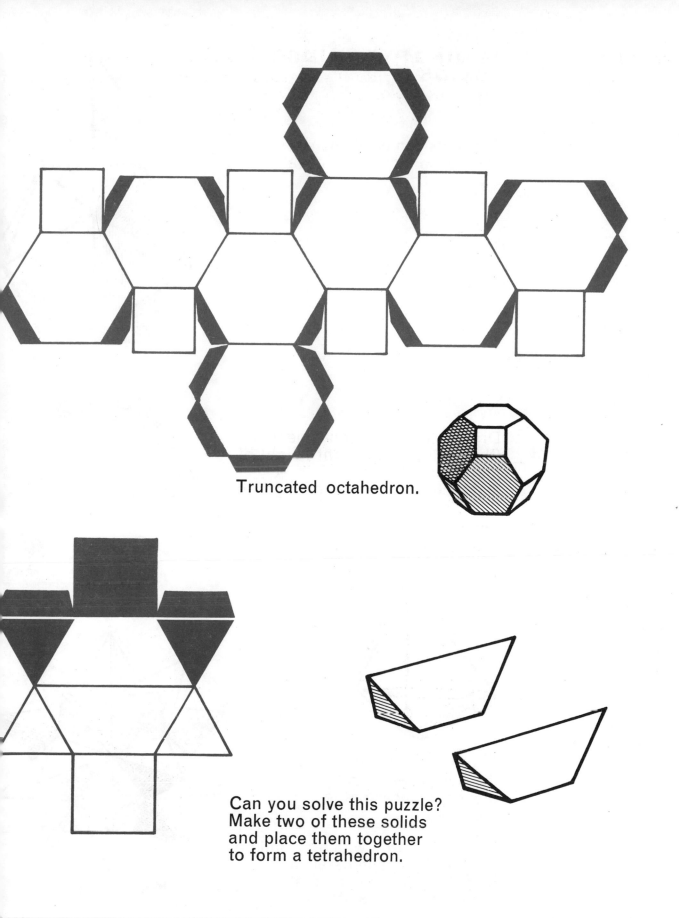

Truncated octahedron.

Can you solve this puzzle?
Make two of these solids
and place them together
to form a tetrahedron.

ADDING PYRAMIDS TO SOLIDS

Pyramids can easily be made to fit on each face of an icosahedron.

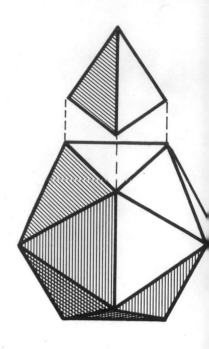

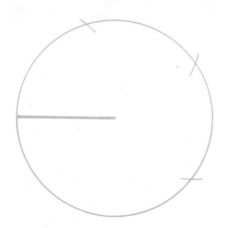

Draw a circle of a convenient size (the radius is the slant height of the pyramid). Mark off three distances each equal in length to the edge of one face of the icosahedron.

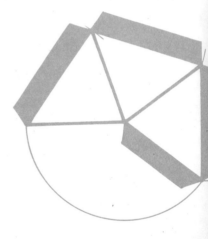

Join the lines and add flaps to the sides.

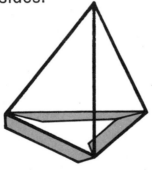

Score each line and fold. Turn the flaps inward and paste to one of the faces of the icosahedron.

An icosahedron with a pyramid on each face is called stellated because it resembles a star. (Latin: stella . . . a star)

The dodecahedron has twelve pentagonal faces.

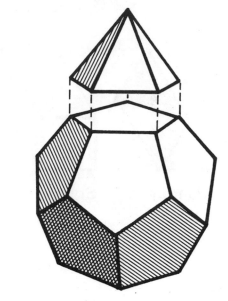

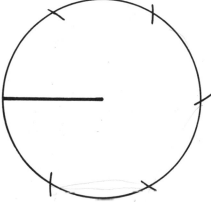

For a five sided pyramid mark off five distances, each distance equal in length to the edge of one face of the dodecahedron.

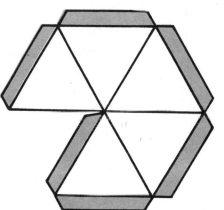

Join the lines and add flaps.

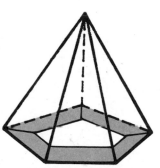

Turn the flaps inward and paste to one face of the dodecahedron.

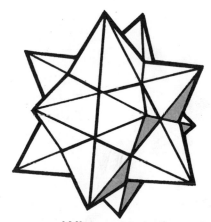

When each face has a pentagonal pyramid the solid is called a stellated dodecahedron.

PRISMS

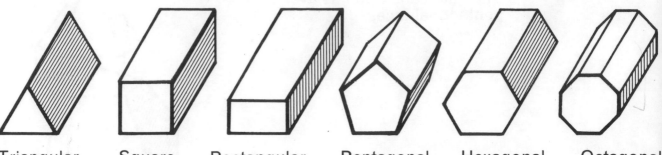

| Triangular prism | Square prism | Rectangular prism | Pentagonal prism | Hexagonal prism | Octagonal prism |

A prism is named from the shape formed at its end. The sides of the prism are parallel and can be any length.

This diagram shows the net of an hexagonal prism with the necessary flaps added to enable it to be assembled.

Can you make the other prisms?

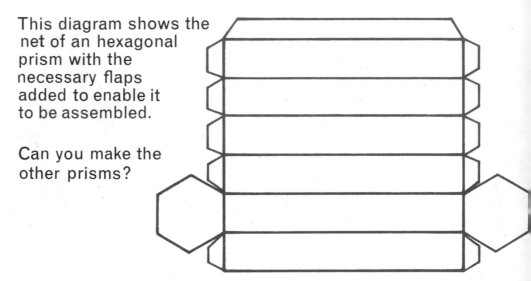

Complete the table below for all the solids you have made.

Name of solid	Number of faces (F)	Number of vertices (V)	Number of edges (E)
Tetrahedron	4	4	6
Cube			
Octahedron			
Dodecahedron			
Icosahedron			
etc.			

A man named Euler who died in 1783 discovered a relationship between the number of faces, vertices and edges and wrote it as

$$F + V = E + 2$$

Can you explain this further?

PLASTICINE SOLIDS

 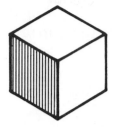  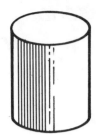

Can you name these solids?
What can you say about them?

The first solid is a sphere. It is a perfect shape because it looks the same no matter from where you view it—from above, from below or from the front.

Make a sphere from plasticine. Drop it gently on your desk.
What shape does the flat part make?
Roll the plasticine into a sphere again and hit the desk hard with it in several different places.
Are the flat parts all the same shape?
Using a sharp knife or a thin piece of wire, remove a slice of the sphere. What do you notice about the flat shape?
Make a sphere again. However hard you hit or whether you slice it with a knife It is only possible to make one flat or plane shape. What is that shape?

The Cylinder
Make a plasticine cylinder.
What new shape is revealed when the cylinder is sliced as shown.

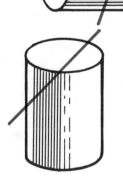

 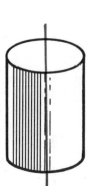

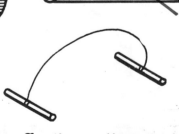

An effective cutter can be made by attaching a fine wire to two toggles.

PLASTICINE SOLIDS

On a coin or small tin lid build
a cone in plasticine.
If a tin lid is used put the
plasticine on the top or outside
of the lid.

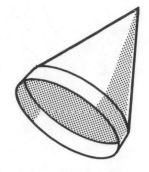

Using a piece of fine wire cut sections of the cone and
make drawings of the new faces you have made.

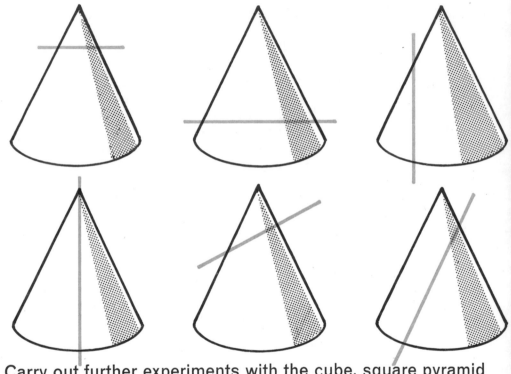

Carry out further experiments with the cube, square pyramid
and triangular pyramid.

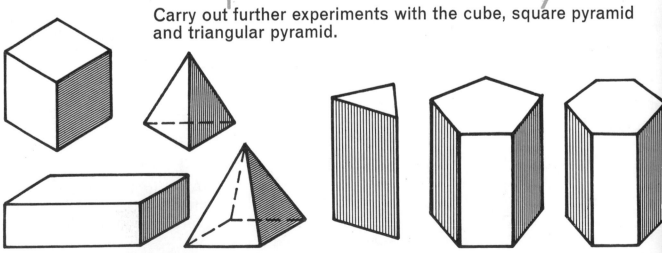

VOLUME

To find the volume of an object it is necessary to measure how much space it occupies.

Solids occupy space.

If you were to hold a marble in one hand and a tennis ball in the other, it is possible to tell at once which—the marble or the ball—takes up most space.

Just as area was measured in *square* units volume is measured in *cubic* units.

Using 1 cm squared paper make three separate 1 cm cubes as follows:

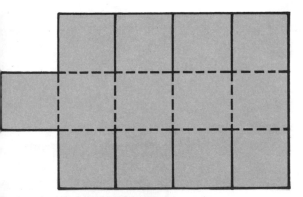 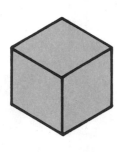

Fold along the dotted lines and cut along the black lines.

The two flaps marked X are pasted last to seal the cube.

Each of these has a volume of one cubic centimetre which is written 1 cm³.

Working in groups arrange 12 centimetre cubes in as many ways as possible.

Here are some suggestions.

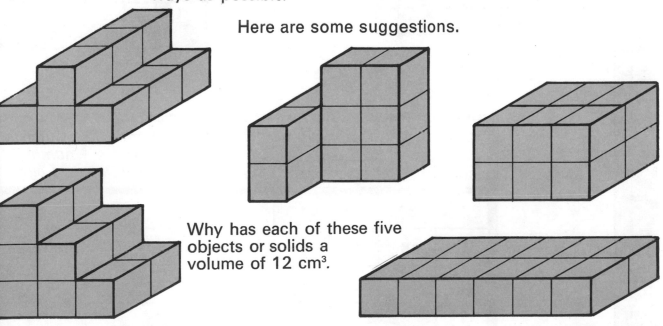

Why has each of these five objects or solids a volume of 12 cm³.

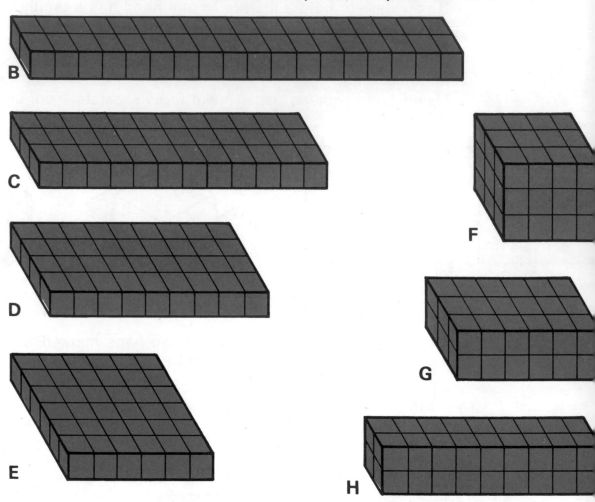

When the object or solid is in the form of a rectangular block it is quite easy to calculate its volume.
Each of the following rectangular blocks was made using 36 cubic centimetres.
Look at each block carefully and complete the table below.

Name of solid	length l	breadth b	height h	Number of cubes in one layer	Number of layers	Total number of cm³
A	36	1	1	1	36	36
B	18	2	1			36
C						
D						

VOLUME

Solids like these shown here have 3 dimensions—height, length and breadth.

The product of any two of these will give the number of cubes in one layer.

The third factor is the number of layers.

First build the following models using 1cm cubes and then complete the table below.

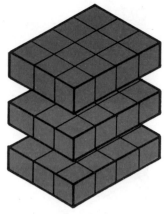

4 × 3 in each of 3 layers.
(4 × 3) × 3.
12 × 3.
36 cubes.

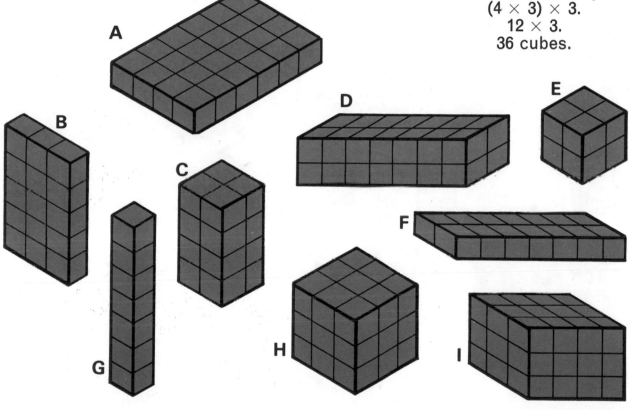

Name of solid	length (l)	breadth (b)	height (h)	l × b × h	Total number of cm³
A	6	4	1	6 × 4 × 1	24
B					
C					
D					

51

VOLUME

Calculate how many one centimetre cubes will be required just to fill the boxes shown below.
The boxes are not drawn to scale and all the measurements shown are centimetres.

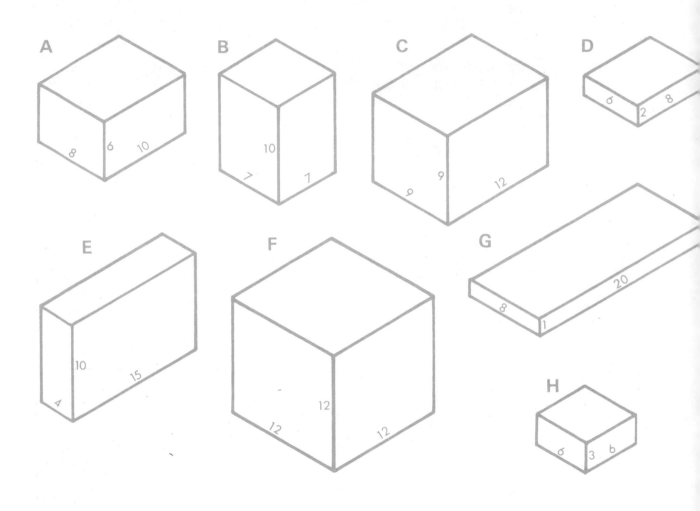

Make a table to record your findings.

	Height	Length	Breadth	Volume in cm³
A				
B				
C				
D				
E				

Make and complete this table.

Height in cm	Length in cm	Breadth in cm	Volume in cm³
3	2	5	
4	1	7	
3		2	48
2	6	3	
5	4		120
	9	1	36

52

HOW CUBES GROW

When each edge on a rectangular block has the same length
it is called a cube: it is a regular solid because each edge, each
face and each corner (or vertex) is the same.
Using one cm squared paper make the following blocks.
They can also be made using Cuisenaire rods or Dienes Apparatus.

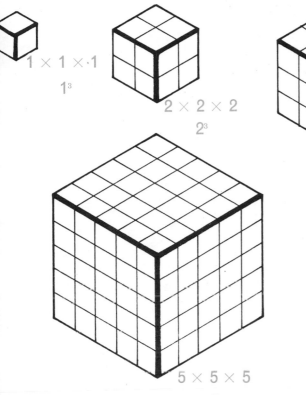

$1 \times 1 \times \cdot 1$
1^3

$2 \times 2 \times 2$
2^3

$3 \times 3 \times 3$
3^3

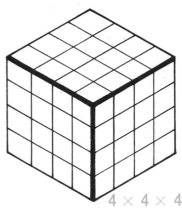

$4 \times 4 \times 4$
4^3

$5 \times 5 \times 5$
5^3

Edge of cube in cm	Volume in cm³
1	1
2	8
3	
4	
5	
6	
7	
8	
9	
10	

Make and complete
the table on the
left and make a
graph to show how
cubes grow.

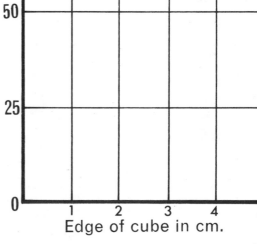

Edge of cube in cm.

Volume of cube in cm³.

MAKING A MEASURING JAR

Solids like stones and pieces of metal are so irregular in shape that it is necessary to devise other methods of finding their volume.

One method is to measure the volume of water they displace and for this purpose a simple measuring jar can be made as follows. Use 1 cm squared paper or card to make a container with a capacity of 20 cm³.

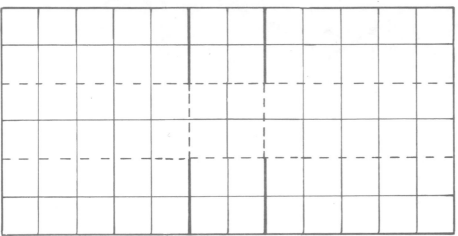

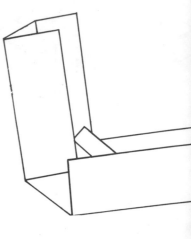

Fold along the dotted lines and cut along the black lines. Assemble the container and coat with varnish or melted candle wax to make it water proof. Containers of this size and shape are also available made in plastic.

Take a selection of differently shaped jars and paste a strip of plain paper to the outside.

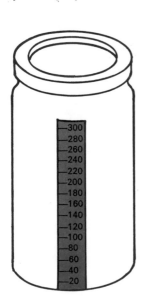

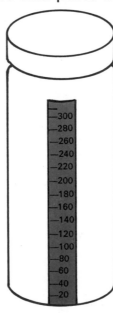

Using the container pour 20 cm³ of water into each jar and mark off on the paper strip the level of the water.

Repeat this until the whole of the paper strip is marked off.

Discuss with your teacher the advantages and disadvantages of each shape of jar.

USING THE MEASURING JAR TO FIND THE VOLUME OF SMALL IRREGULAR SOLIDS

Make a collection of solids which are heavier than water and are not too big to go in the jar. At the side of each solid place a one centimetre cube and discuss with your friends what you think the volume of each solid is in cm³. Fill the jar with water to a convenient level and drop the solid into the jar.
Record your findings in the form of a table.

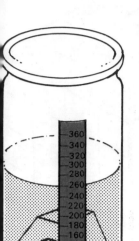

Name of solid	Estimated Volume in cm³	Level of water in jar		Volume of solid in cm³.
		Before	After	
Nut and bolt				
Pebble				
Piece of coal				

Collect a number of vessels such as egg cup, tea cup, tumbler, medicine glass, thimble, school milk bottle.
First estimate the capacity in cm³ of each vessel.
Fill each in turn with water, or dry sand, or fine sago, and use the measuring jar to measure these volumes in cm³.
Record your findings in the form of a table.

Name of vessel	Estimated capacity in cm³	Actual capacity in cm³
Egg Cup		
Tumbler		
Milk Jug		

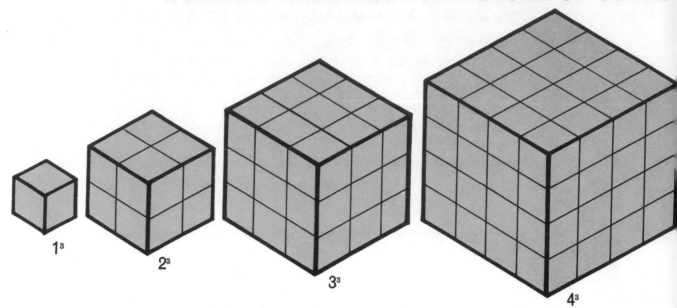

1³ 2³ 3³ 4³

Find the volume and the surface area of the cubes shown above.
Calculate the volume and surface area of cubes with an edge of
(a) 5 cm. (b) 6 cm. (c) 7 cm. (d) 8 cm. (e) 9 cm. (f) 10 cm.

Show your results on a table.

Cube	Volume	Surface area	$\dfrac{Volume}{Surface\ area}$
1³	1	6	$\frac{1}{6}$
2³	8	24	$\frac{1}{3}$
3³	27	54	$\frac{1}{2}$
4³	64	96	
5³	125		
6³	216		
7³			
8³			
9³			
10³			

BASIC CONSTRUCTIONS

The making of geometric patterns can be both fascinating and rewarding.

The successful completion of such patterns will largely depend on how familiar you are with certain basic constructions.

The standard of your work will reflect the condition of your drawing instruments. You will need a fairly hard pencil (H or 2H), a good quality ruler or straight edge and a pair of undamaged compasses.

Always work with a sharp pointed pencil. Construction lines and any guide lines should be clearly but lightly drawn.
The right angle is an essential feature of many shapes and can be constructed in several ways.

1. To erect a perpendicular line at A

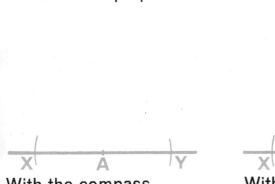  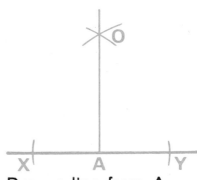

With the compass point at A strike arcs at X and Y.

With centres at X and Y strike intersecting arcs to cut at O.

Draw a line from A through O.
OA is at right angles to X Y.

2. To drop a perpendicular line from O.

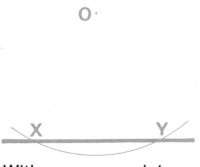 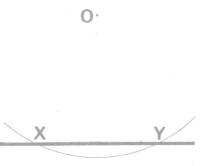 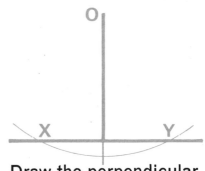

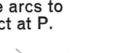

With compass point on O draw an arc to cut the line at X and Y.

With centres at X and Y strike arcs to intersect at P.

Draw the perpendicular.

BASIC CON-
STRUCTIONS

3. To draw a line at right angles to another line.

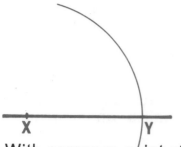

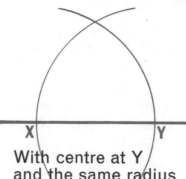

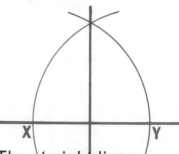

With compass point at X draw an arc cutting the line at Y.

With centre at Y and the same radius draw a second arc.

The straight line joining the intersections of the arcs is at right angles to the original line.

4. To erect a perpendicular at the end of a line.

The construction makes use of the fact that any angle drawn in a semi-circle must be a right angle.

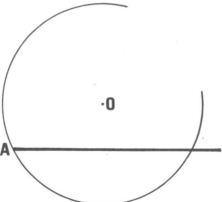

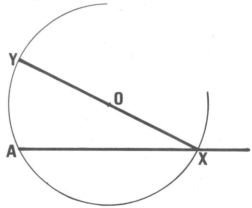

Draw an arc passing through A. The centre of the arc can be anywhere above the line.

Draw a line from X through O to cut the arc again at Y.

It will be seen that AXY is a triangle in a semi-circle. The angle XAY is a right angle.

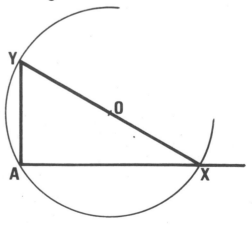

Drawing Rectangles and Squares.

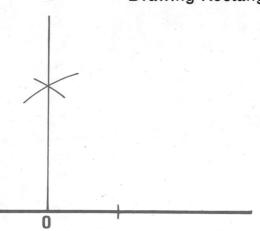

Construct a right angle at O.

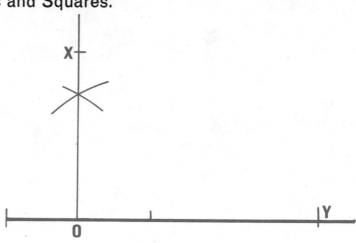

The compasses can now be used to mark off the required distances from O, say 6 cm and 9 cm.

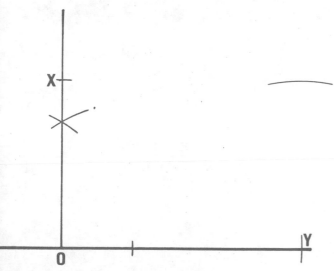

We now want a point which is 6 cm from Y and 9 cm from X. With centre at Y draw an arc with radius 6 cm. All the points on this arc are 6 cm from Y.

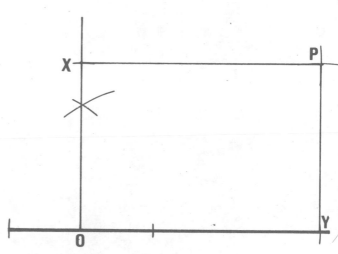

With centre at X draw an arc with a radius of 9 cm. The point where the two arcs intersect is 9 cm from X and 6 cm from Y. XPYO is a rectangle measuring 6 cm by 9 cm.

Discuss with your teacher how this construction can be used for drawing rectangles of all sizes.

What special kind of rectangle would you obtain if you were to strike off equal distances from 0?

Sometimes it is necessary to draw a regular polygon where the side has to be a certain length, say 7 cm.

The Pentagon

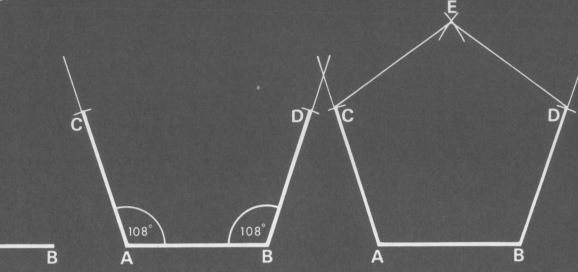

Draw one side of the pentagon 7 cm long.
Call it A B.

Use your protractor to construct angles of 108° at A and B. Mark C and D 7 cm from A and B.

With compass point on C and D and radius 7 cm draw two arcs to intersect at E. Join up C E and D E.

This is an alternative method.

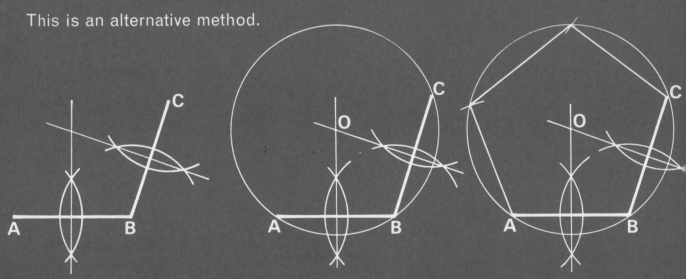

Draw two sides AB and BC at an angle of 108°. Construct perpendicular bisectors.

With the point of intersection O as centre and radius OA draw a circle.

With compasses set at distance AB mark off the remaining three sides of the pentagon on the circumference.

TESSELLATIONS OR TILING

An area can be covered by tiles in many different ways.
Study the geometrical patterns used in linoleum and other
floor coverings, wallpapers, curtain materials, table-cloths etc.
examine buildings for further examples—the rectangular faces
of bricks making up a wall, roof tiles, the different shaped
panes of glass in windows and the smaller patterns found in
semi-opaque glass.

These and many other examples of how shapes are used to
cover surfaces can be seen all around you.

Although there are many combinations of shape to be seen there
are only three regular shapes which, when used alone, will
fit together and completely cover a surface.

Remember a regular shape is one in which all the sides and
angles are equal.

You can discover for yourself which these three shapes are by
studying the interior angles of all regular shapes.

Shape	Number of sides	Interior angle
Triangle	3	60°
Square	4	90°
Pentagon	5	108°
Hexagon	6	120°
Heptagon	7	128$\frac{4}{7}$°
Octagon	8	135°
Nonagon	9	140°
Decagon	10	144°

Which of these angles
can be repeated to make
360° without leaving a
gap?
Which of these are not
true if the figure is
irregular?

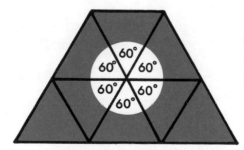

Equilateral triangles will fit
together because each interior
angle is 60°.

The interior angle of a square
is 90°. Four angles of 90° fit
exactly into 360°.

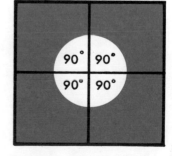

61

TESSELLATIONS OR TILING

Hexagons fit together because the interior angles fit together to make 360°.

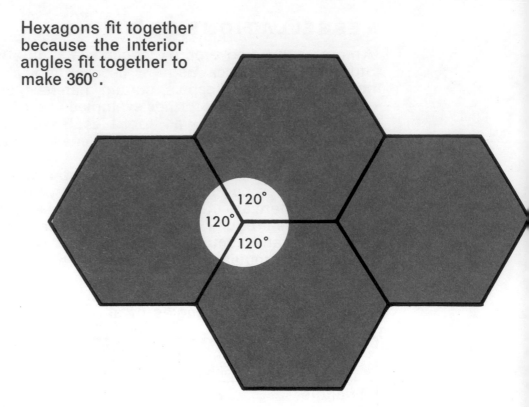

Can you fill space using any other regular shape?

Set of sizes of angles of regular shapes.

$$R = \{ 60°, 90°, 108°, 120°, 128\tfrac{4}{7}°, 135°, \dots\dots\dots\dots \}$$

Set of angles which are exact fractions of 360°.

$$A = \{ 180°, 120°, 90°, 72°, 60°, 51\tfrac{3}{7}°, 45°, \dots\dots\dots\dots \}$$

An area can be filled exactly with regular shapes provided that the interior angles fit exactly into 360°.

$$R \cap A = \{ 60°, 90°, 120° \}$$

There are only three possible shapes.

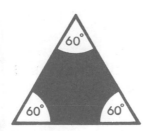

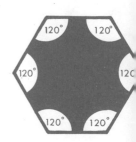

Combinations of regular shapes make interesting tessellations. The following tessellations are made by combining two or three of these regular shapes.

It will be seen that the sides of each shape measure the same.
Make a copy of each shape on a stout card by drawing or tracing and cut them out.
Use these cut out shapes as templates to draw round and build up the patterns below.

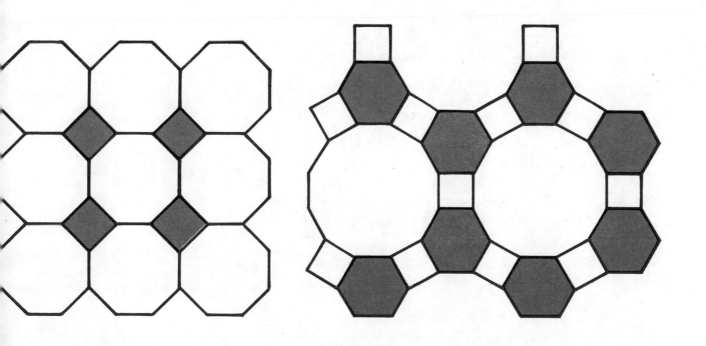

The word tessellate means "to pave with small blocks of stone forming a pattern."

A tessellation is a mosaic.

A variety of irregular shapes can be used to make tessellations: many of them can be constructed with ruler and compasses.

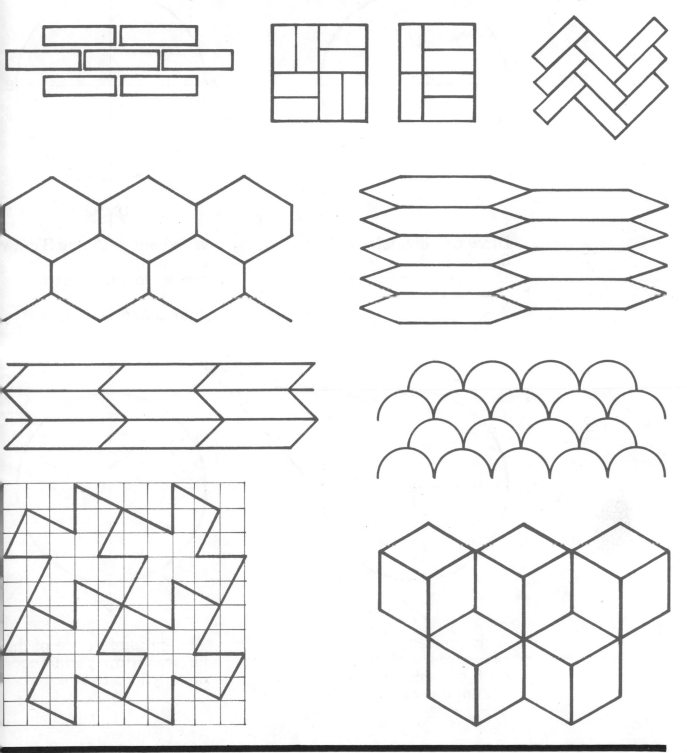

PATTERNS WITH CIRCLES

It is frequently necessary to partition the circumference of a circle into twelve equal parts.
Here is one way of doing this.

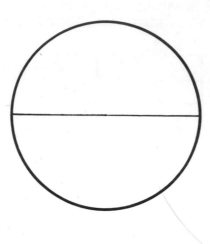

Draw one diameter of the circle.

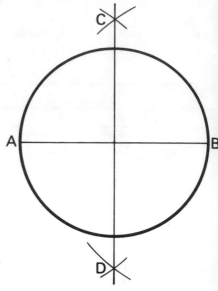

With centres A and B draw arcs with the same radius to intersect at C and D.
Join C and D.

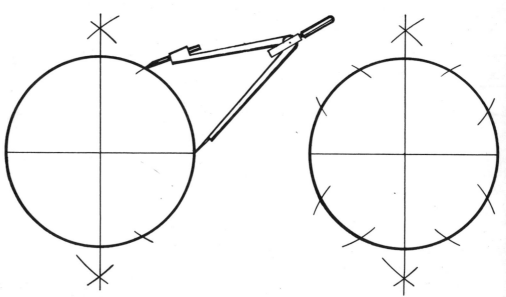

With compass set at the radius of the circle mark off the points on the circumference as shown.

The circumference of the circle is now partitioned equally into twelve parts.

Here is one method of partitioning the circumference of a
circle into sixteen parts.

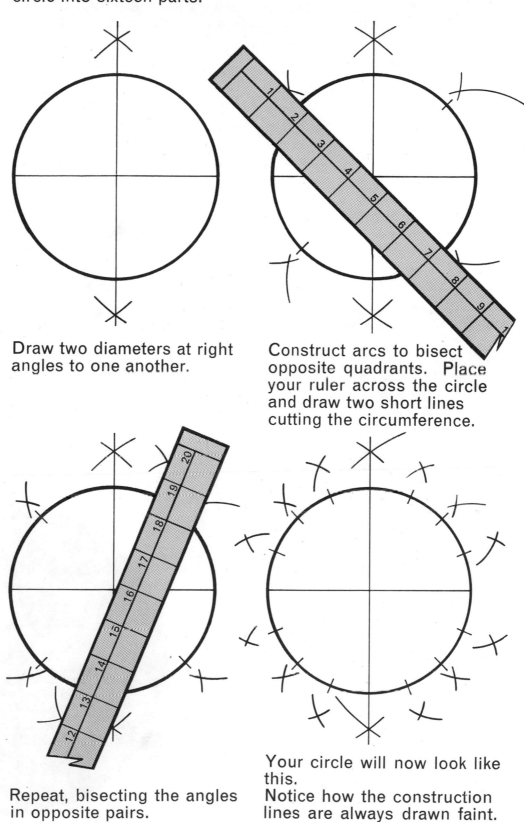

Draw two diameters at right
angles to one another.

Construct arcs to bisect
opposite quadrants. Place
your ruler across the circle
and draw two short lines
cutting the circumference.

Repeat, bisecting the angles
in opposite pairs.

Your circle will now look like
this.
Notice how the construction
lines are always drawn faint.

PATTERNS WITH CIRCLES

These designs are based on twelve points drawn at equal distances on the circumference.
More complex designs can be drawn by increasing the number of points on the circumference.

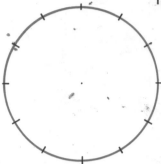

Partition the circumference of the base circle into twelve equal parts.

Draw six circles using alternate points as centres so that each circle passes through the centre of the original circle.

Use the remaining points as centres for six more circles.

68

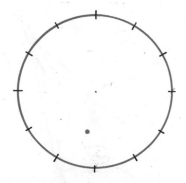

Partition the base circle as before and mark a point inside the circle.
The finished effect is better if this point lies mid-way between any two points on the circumference. Discuss with your teacher how you would find such a point.

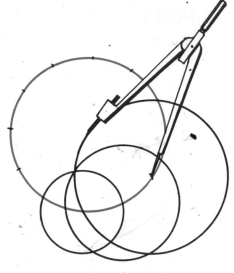

Using each of the twelve points as centres draw circles, each one passing through the point marked inside the circle.

PATTERNS
WITH CIRCLES

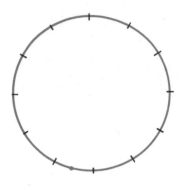

Partition the circumference of the base circle into twelve equal parts as before. Mark a point mid-way between any two points on the circumference.

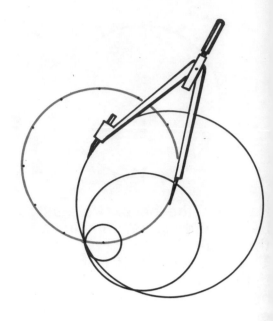

Using each of the twelve points as centres draw circles, each one passing through the point marked on the circumference.

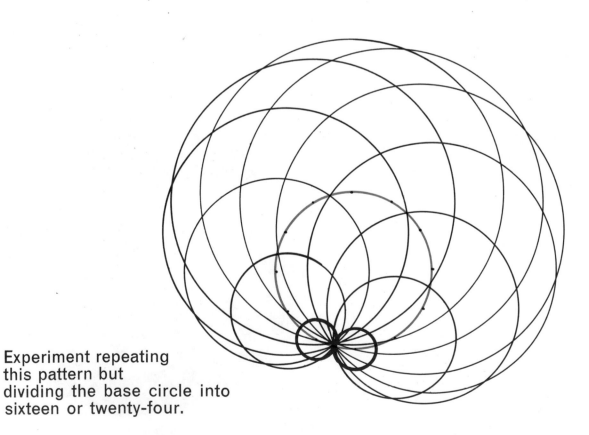

Experiment repeating this pattern but dividing the base circle into sixteen or twenty-four.

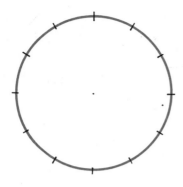

Partition the circumference of the circle as before. Mark a point outside the base circle mid-way between any two adjacent points on the circumference.

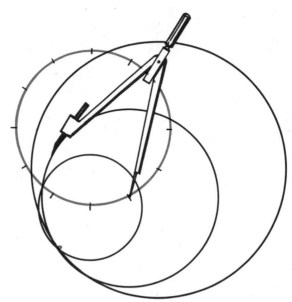

With the twelve points as centres draw circles, each one passing through the point marked outside the circle.

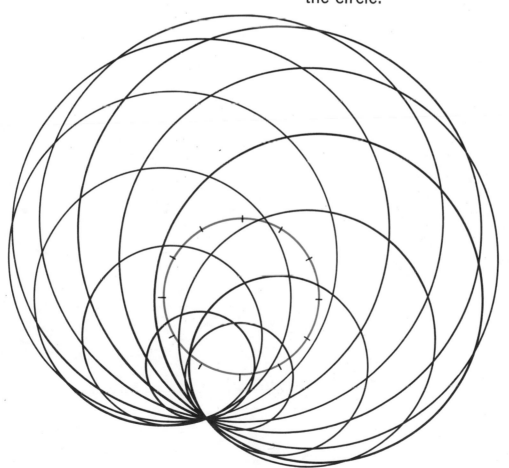

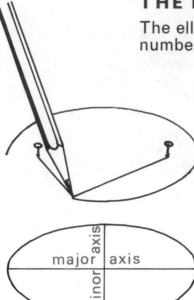

THE ELLIPSE

The ellipse is a fascinating shape and can be drawn in a number of ways.

Stick two pins in a board about 5 centimetres apart.

To each pin fasten the end of a piece of thin string about 7 centimetres long. Put the pencil point as shown in the diagram and, keeping the string taut, draw round the pins.

The shape you draw is an ellipse.

The line passing through the two points made by the pins is called the major axis.

The line at right angles through the mid point of the major axis is called the minor axis.

Using the same length of string draw a number of ellipses putting the pins closer together each time.

What shape is obtained when the two pins coincide?

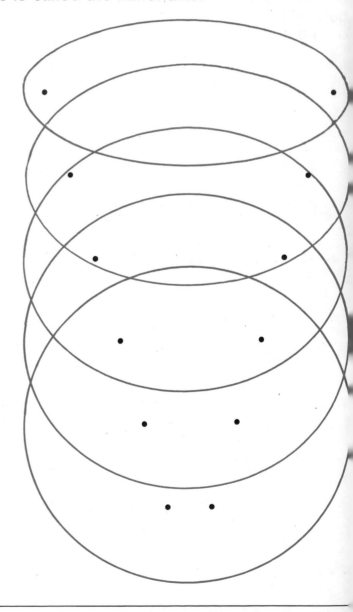

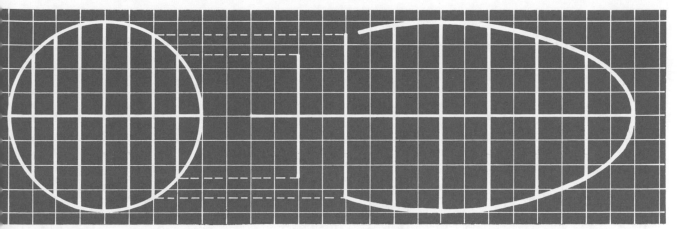

Draw a circle on 1 cm squared paper and mark the vertical lines and the diameter.

On a line twice the length of the diameter draw the vertical lines at 2 cm intervals.

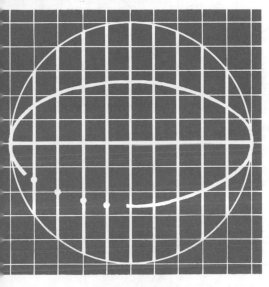

On squared paper draw a circle and mark in the vertical lines. Rule in a diameter. On each vertical line mark in the mid point between the diameter and the circumference.

Join these points.

Is it necessary to use the points halfway between the diameter and the circumference?

Would any fraction do?

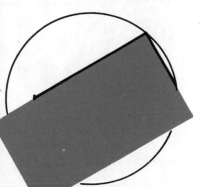

Draw a circle and mark a point on the diameter. Place a rectangular card so that it touches this point and the circumference. Draw the right angle.

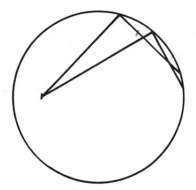

Repeat this a number of times.

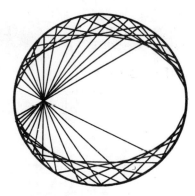

The intersections of the lines make an ellipse.

PATTERNS
WITH CIRCLES

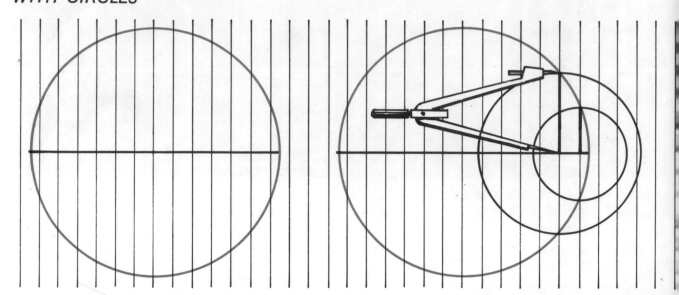

Draw a circle (called the base circle) on lined exercise paper with a radius equal to 6½ spaces. Ensure that the centre of this base circle lies on one of the lines.

Draw circles each one having as radius the length measured between the diameter of the base circle and its circumference.

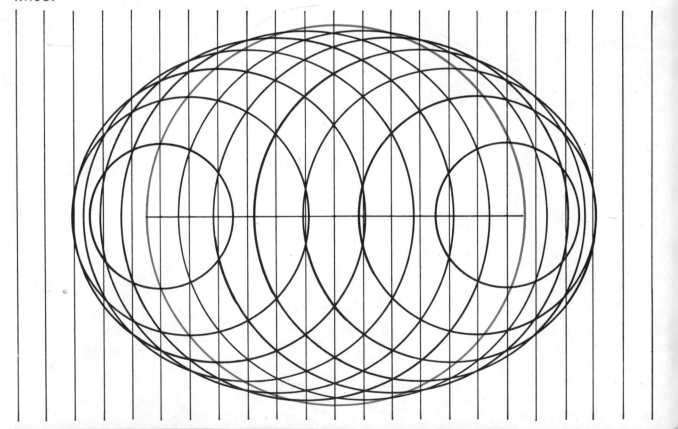

FOR ODD MOMENTS

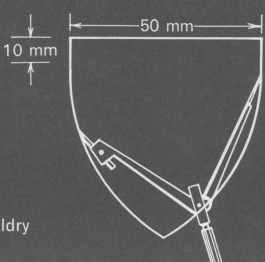

Geometry in History and Heraldry

THE PARABOLA

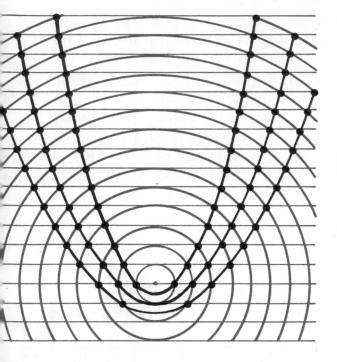

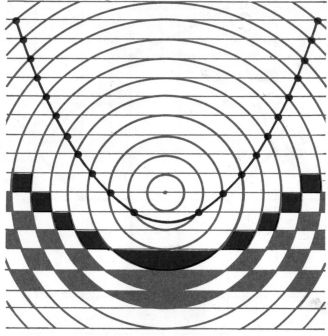

On a piece of lined exercise paper draw a number of concentric circles. Plot the points where the circles cut the lines and join them to make a parabolic curve.

Draw one parabolic curve and colour in the shapes as shown to make a design.

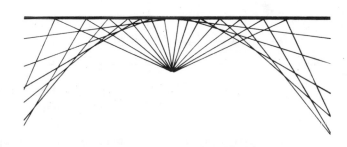

Draw a straight line and mark a point about 2 cm from it. Place a rectangular piece of card (a post-card is suitable) so that one edge touches this point and one right angled corner touches the line. Draw two lines as shown.

Move the card a short distance and draw two more lines. Repeat this until the shape of a parabolic curve is made.

TO FIND THE AREA OF A SHAPE ON A LATTICE

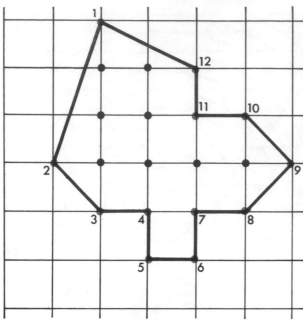

To find the area of this shape first count the number of vertices on the perimeter of the shape (those coloured red).

Now count the points of intersection enclosed by the shape (those coloured black).

The area can now be found by taking half the number of vertices on the perimeter, adding the number of points of intersection enclosed by the shape and subtracting one whole one.

$$\frac{12}{2} + 8 - 1 = 13 \text{ squares.}$$

You will find a geo-board or nail board ideal for setting out shapes of this kind.

Record your shapes on squared paper.

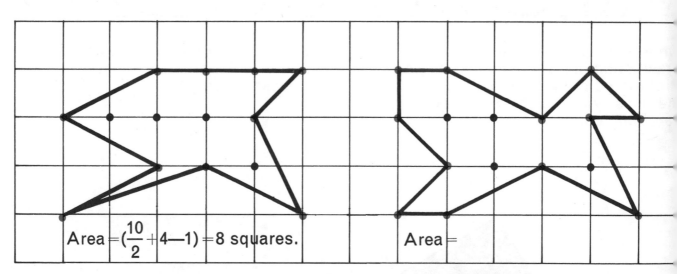

Area $= (\frac{10}{2} + 4 - 1) = 8$ squares.   Area $=$

Find the area of the following shapes and then experiment with shapes of your own design.

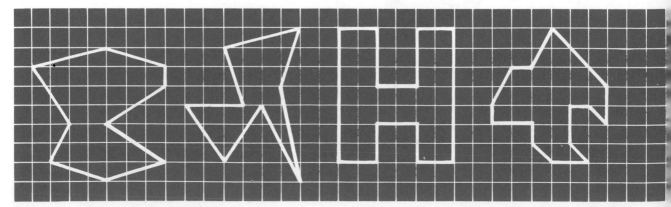

78

DIVIDING A LINE INTO A NUMBER OF EQUAL PARTS

Parallel lines can be used to divide a line into any number of equal parts.

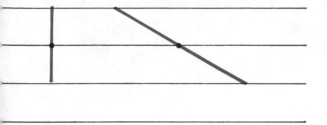

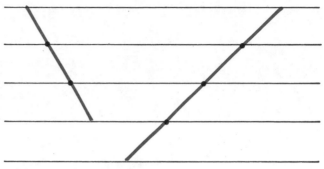

Use a ruler or a strip of paper to test whether the red lines have been divided equally by the parallel lines.

This method can be used to divide a line of any length into any number of equal parts.

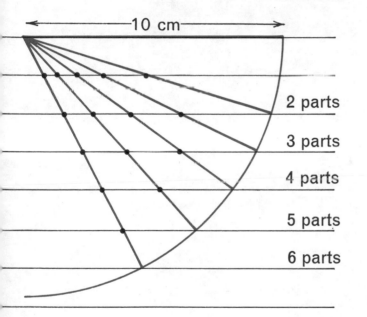

To divide a line into 3, 4, 5, 6 or 7 equal parts.
With the compasses set at 10 cm draw an arc on a sheet of ruled exercise paper so that it cuts across at least 7 lines.

Join up the lines as shown.

In this way divide lines measuring 8 cm, 10 cm and 12 cm each into 4, 5, and 6 parts.

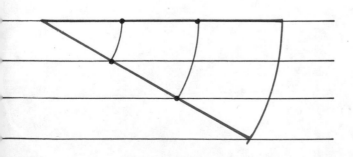

This line has been divided into 3 equal parts.

Can you see similar shapes?

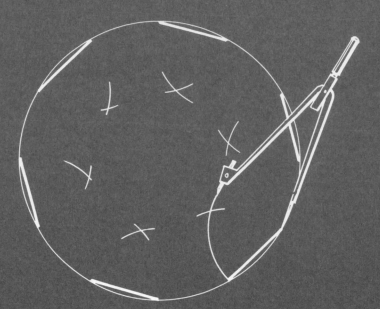

On thin card draw a circle and partition the circumference into twelve equal parts as explained on page 66. Draw in alternate chords and with the compass set at a distance equal to that of a chord mark in six sets of intersecting arcs.

Mark in the remaining six chords to complete the dodecagon Add lines as shown to obtain six congruent quadrilaterals.

1. Cut out the twelve quadrilaterals

2. Draw a second dodecagon exactly the same size as that shown above and cut it out.

3. Use the twelve congruent quadrilaterals and the dodecagon together to make one large dodecagon.

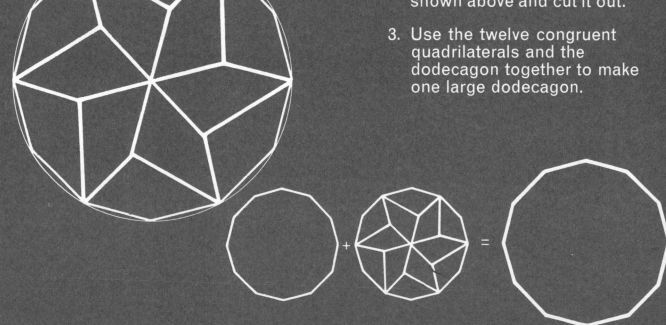

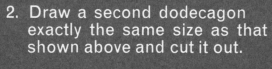

ROTATIONAL SYMMETRY

Rotational symmetry as the name suggests has to do with shapes turning or spinning round.

Some shapes take up the same position several times when rotating through one revolution, depending of course, on their design and shape.

Examples of rotational symmetry are to be found in many patterns and also in Nature.

Find a square tin box and mark one corner of the lid clearly.

The diagrams show the different positions in which the lid can be placed on the tin.

Because the lid will fit in four different positions it is said to have rotational symmetry of order four.

Make a collection of boxes with detachable lids and experimen to find how many different ways each lid will fit on its box. The answer will give the order of rotational symmetry of that particular shape.

Construct or trace one or more of the following shapes in thin card.

Mark in the angles and cut out the shapes.

The circles shown are construction lines.

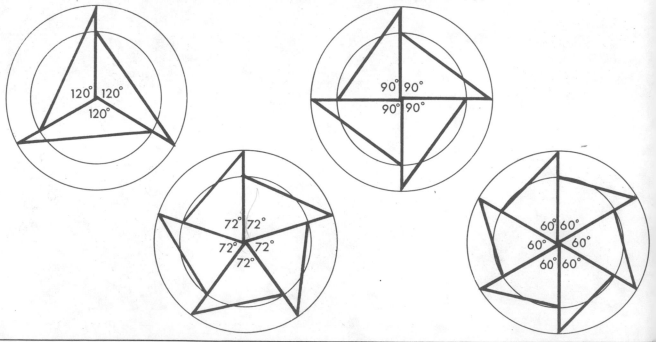

ROTATIONAL SYMMETRY

Colour one corner of this shape. Hold it at the centre using the steel point of a pair of compasses.

Rotate the shape until it takes up the same position.

Rotate until it again takes up the same position.

This shape takes up the same position three times when making one complete revolution or rotation.
It has rotational symmetry of order three.

What is the order of rotational symmetry of the following shapes?

THE SYMMETRY OF REGULAR SHAPES

When a shape is rotated about a central point so that the shape again takes the same outline as before, the shape is said to have "rotational symmetry" about that point and the point is called "the centre of rotation".

Make copies of the following regular shapes.

Take each shape in turn and draw round it to obtain an outline on a sheet of plain paper.

Put a spot in one corner to help you to identify the position of the shape as it is rotated.

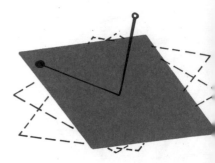

Place the cut-out shape exactly over its outline. Hold it down with a pin or the point of a compass placed at the centre of rotation. Then slowly turn the shape until it once again exactly covers the outline.

This shape will have been rotated through an angle. This will be made clearer if a line is drawn from the centre of the shape t the spot in the corner.

Can you see from these diagrams the size of the angle of rotation for each shape as it turns to fit again on to its own outline?

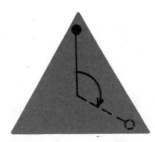 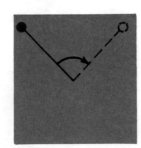 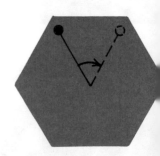

The number of times a shape fits on to itself as it rotates through 360° **is** its "order of rotational symmetry".

Why do some shapes fit **on** to themselves more times than others in rotating through 360°?

Can you see the relationship between the angle of rotation and the order of rotational symmetry?

Make and complete the following table.

Name of shape	Number of sides	Angle of rotation	Order of rotational symmetry
Equilateral triangle			
Square			
Hexagon			

When a square is rotated through one right angle it will again take the same position.

Study these diagrams and notice the angle of rotation for each position.

No rotation.

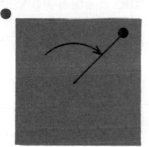

Rotation through one right angle.

Rotation through two right angles.

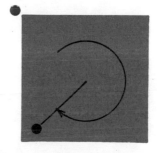

Rotation through three right angles.

When regular shapes can be folded so that the two halves are congruent—one half can be fitted exactly over the other half—the shape is said to be symmetrical about the line of the fold.
The fold is sometimes referred to as the line of symmetry or the axis of symmetry.

Draw and cut out a square, an equilateral triangle and a hexagon as shown on page 84
Find in how many ways each shape can be folded along an axis of symmetry. The folds will now show the different axes of symmetry.

Why do some shapes have more axes of symmetry than others?

SYMMETRY

It is sometimes necessary to give a name to each axis of symmetry. In the square shown below two axes are named. Can you name the other two?

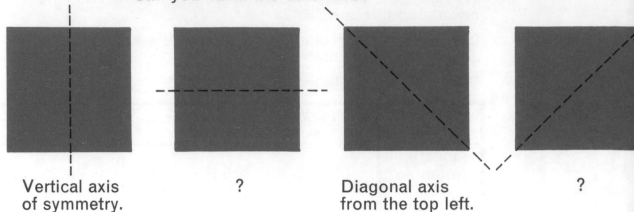

Vertical axis
of symmetry.

?

Diagonal axis
from the top left.

?

The *axis of symmetry* can be thought of as a line about which the shape can be *turned over* so that it will again come round to take up the same outline as before.

Here is a simple way to help you to understand what happens when a shape turns over.

Cut out a square and put a spot in one corner and immediately behind the spot on the reverse side put a cross. The reverse side of the square could also be given a different colour in order to show when it has been turned over.

Bend a pipe cleaner over so that it will grip the square along its axis of symmetry.

When the pipe cleaner is turned between the finger and thumb the square will turn over to take up the same outline as before.

The direction in which the square turns will depend along which axis of symmetry the pipe cleaner lies.

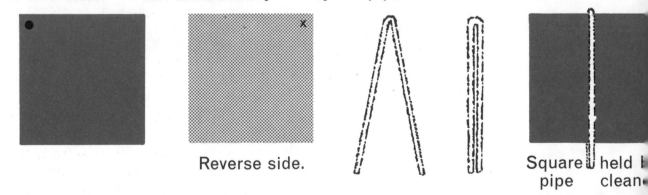

Reverse side.

Square held b
pipe clean

Try placing the pipe cleaner along different axes of symmetry and turning the square over. If the pipe cleaner is held in the same position all the time you will find that the square returns exactly to the same position as before.

It may help if the top of the pipe cleaner is held steady by placing it against the end of a finger whilst it is turned by the fingers of the other hand.

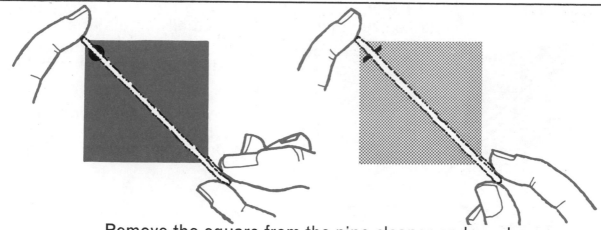

Remove the square from the pipe cleaner and see how many different ways it can be *turned over* and put down on the table to fit its own outline.

Now let us see how we can arrive at these positions using the pipe cleaner, always beginning with the spot in the top left hand corner.

 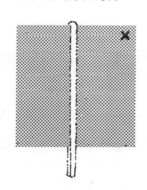

First put the pipe cleaner along the vertical axis and observe what happens when the square is turned through 180°.

The spot takes up a position as far to the right of the axis (shown by the pipe cleaner) as it was to the left.

Hold a mirror along the axis and the spot is in the same position as the image in the mirror—on the other side of the square.

Because of this, we sometimes refer to this movement as "reflecting the square".

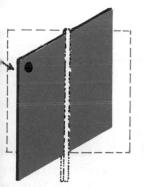 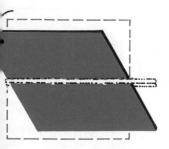 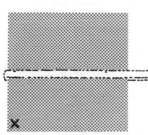

Put the pipe cleaner along the horizontal axis. Can you see where the spot will come when the square is "reflected along the horizontal axis"?
Once again the spot is as far below the axis as it was above—and on the other side of the square.
The square is reflected through 180° along the horizontal axis of symmetry.

When the square is reflected along the top left diagonal axis it will be seen that the spot is actually on the axis.

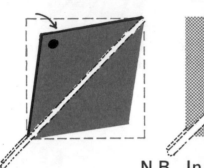
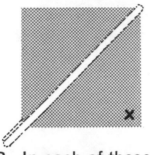

When the square is turned over along this axis the spot moves very little.

Why is this?

A point on a wheel near the centre does not turn through as great a distance as a point near the circumference.

When the pipe cleaner is placed along the diagonal axis from the top right hand corner, the corner marked by the spot moves across to the bottom left hand corner, which is exactly the same distance from the pipe cleaner as it was before.

N.B. In each of these "reflections" the outline of the square is the same before and after it has been turned over. Discuss this with your teacher and experiment again with the pipe cleaner to see if it is true.

Remove the square from the pipe cleaner and place it on your desk with the spot in the top left hand corner. Make an outline on a sheet of plain paper.

Find in how many different positions you can replace the square in the outline with the spot showing.

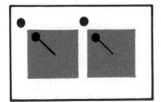
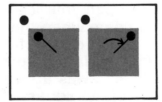
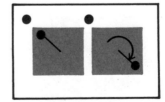
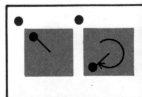

Now let us think what we have to do to the square to put it in each of these positions always starting with the spot in the top left hand corner.

Each diagram shows the position of the square from which it is to be rotated.

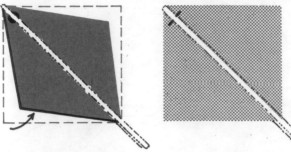

It is left in the
same position.
No rotation.

Rotation
through 90°.

Rotation
through 180°.

Rotation
through 270°.

Now examine how the positions of the square are arrived at when it has been "turned over" or "reflected".
The study of these "reflections" is made easier if you actually turn the square over either with your fingers or with the pipe cleaner.

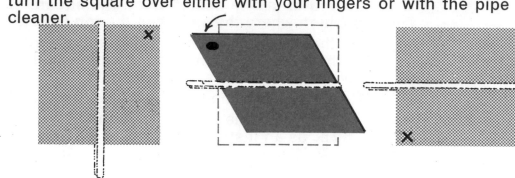

Reflect the square along the vertical axis of symmetry.

Reflect the square along the horizontal axis of symmetry.

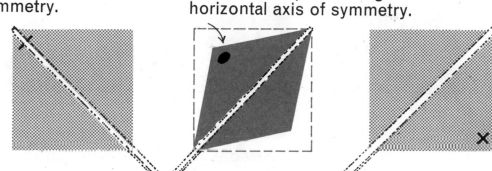

Reflect the square along the top left diagonal.

Reflect the square along the top right diagonal.

Accustom yourself to using the correct language when describing how each different position of the square has been reached.

e.g. The square has been rotated through one right angle.
The square has been reflected along the vertical axis.

Write out in full what you would have to do to put the square in these positions always starting from position 1.

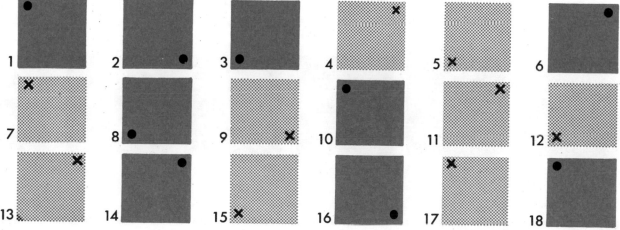

We have seen that a square can be "fitted on to itself" in eight different ways and that each of these positions can be arrived at in one operation on the square beginning from the position where the spot is in the top left hand corner.

So that we can refer both to the *movement* and the *position* of the square brought about by the movement we are going to give each position a suitable name.

Remember that the name will have two purposes:

    a. as a name for the position.
    b. as an instruction to make a particular movement.

Examine these four positions and their names.

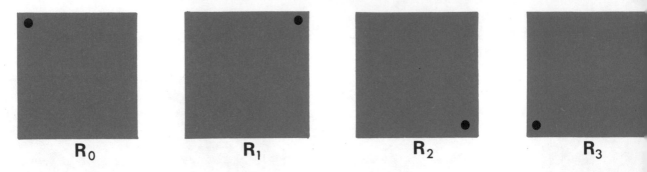

R_0 R_1 R_2 R_3

These positions can now be referred to by their names shown above.

The symbols R_0 R_1 R_2 R_3 are also to be used as instructions

R_0 means "leave alone" or "leave it as you found it".

R_1 is an instruction to "rotate through one right angle".

R_2 is an instruction to "rotate through two right angles".

R_3 is an instruction to "rotate through three right angles".

What will the position of the squares shown below be:—

    a. If you leave them as they are? (That is, operate R_0)
    b. If you follow the instruction R_1 R_2 R_3 on each position i
       turn.

Now examine the positions brought about by "reflecting" the squares. The square has been "turned" or "reflected", so each movement is called T.

The short stroke accompanying each T shows the direction of the axis of symmetry about which the square has been turned or reflected.

The dotted line is the axis.

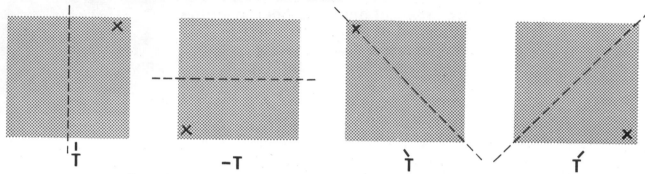

$\overset{|}{T}$ $-T$ $\overset{\backslash}{T}$ $\overset{/}{T}$

Put the square in each of the following positions. Write down the names of the movement which will return the square to the position named R_0.

Example No. 6 T

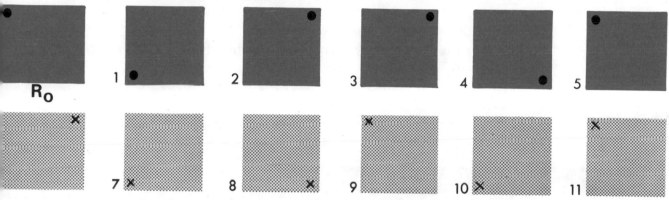

Now examine the following diagrams and find which *two* movements will take the square from R_0 to those shown. There is more than one way of doing this.

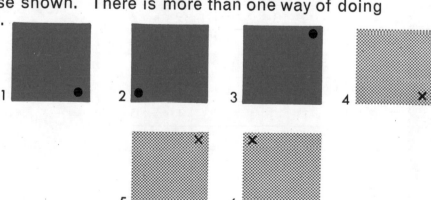

MAKING A TABLE OF MOVEMENTS

1 Discuss this table with your teacher. It is the kind of table you made in the first year.

The numbers shown in reverse colour give the sum of a number from the horizontal set and a number from the vertical set of numbers.

Can you see a number which, when added to another number, has no effect?

Look at these equations. Do they help you?

$0 + 3 = 3 \quad 0 + 2 = 2 \quad 0 + 1 = 1$

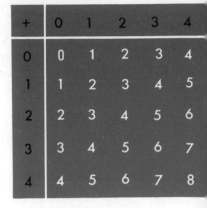

+	0	1	2	3	4
0	0	1	2	3	4
1	1	2	3	4	5
2	2	3	4	5	6
3	3	4	5	6	7
4	4	5	6	7	8

Copy the table above and put a ring round any "answer number" which is not given in either the horizontal or vertical set of numbers.

What is the name of the operation being performed?

2. MAKING A TABLE OF MOVEMENTS

Think of a clock. It takes 5 hours for the hour hand to turn from 12 (or 0) to show 5 o'clock.

Where will the hour hand point after another 10 hours have passed?

In a clock 5 hours + 10 hours shows 3 hours after 12.

Where will the hour hand point after turning from 12 through

a. 7 hrs. and then 9 hrs.
b. 2 hrs. and then 3 hrs.
c. 6 hrs. and then 7 hrs.
d. 10 hrs. and then 3 hrs.
e. 8 hrs. and then 8 hrs.
f. 10 hrs. and then 11 hrs.

⊕	0	1	2	3	4	5	6	7	8	9	10	11	12
0	0	1	2	3	4	5	6	7	8	9	10	11	12
1	1	2	3	4	5	6	7	8	9	10	11	12	1
2	2	3	4	5	6	7	8	9	10	11	12	1	2
3	3	4	5	6	7	8	9	10	11	12	1	2	3
4	4	5	6	7	8	9	10	11	12	1	2	3	4
5	5	6	7	8	9	10	11	12	1	2	3	4	5
6	6	7	8	9	10	11	12	1	2	3	4	5	6
7	7	8	9	10	11	12	1	2	3	4	5	6	7
8	8	9	10	11	12	1	2	3	4	5	6	7	8
9	9	10	11	12	1	2	3	4	5	6	7	8	9
10	10	11	12	1	2	3	4	5	6	7	8	9	10
11	11	12	1	2	3	4	5	6	7	8	9	10	11
12	12	1	2	3	4	5	6	7	8	9	10	11	12

Now study this table and discuss these questions with your teacher.

What does the table show?

How would you describe the operation? Is it addition?

Could the operation be described as

"Finding the sum of two numbers and subtracting 12?"
or

"Finding what remains when 12 has been subtracted from the sum of two numbers".

The symbol ∮ could stand for "followed by" so

9 followed by 8 gives 5 or 9 ∮ 8 gives 5

Find all the numbers which in this way give 5.

Is there a number which when added leaves the clock as it was?

Can you find an answer number which is not either in the horizontal or vertical set of numbers?

Here is another clock face but on this one there are only four divisions numbered from 0 to 3.

Make a circle of card, number it as shown and put a pipe cleaner through the centre to act as a pointer (like the hand of a clock).

Set the pointer at 0.

First move it through 1 space and follow this by moving it through 2 spaces. So 1 followed by 2=3 or 1 ∮ 2=3.

In the same way find where the pointer is after carrying out the following operations.

2 ∮ 1   3 ∮ 1   2 ∮ 2   1 ∮ 3

Discuss the following diagrams with your teacher. The table shows where the pointer would be after certain operations have been carried out. Check the tables. Are they correct?

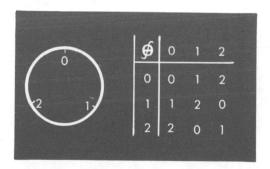

∮	0	1	2
0	0	1	2
1	1	2	0
2	2	0	1

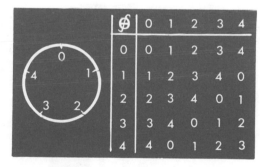

∮	0	1	2	3	4
0	0	1	2	3	4
1	1	2	3	4	0
2	2	3	4	0	1
3	3	4	0	1	2
4	4	0	1	2	3

Make a table when the clock face shows the numbers

a. 0 1 2 3 4 5

b. 0 1 2 3 4 5 6 7 8

Why is this kind of number work sometimes called "remainder arithmetic".

Could you make similar tables to show what the results would be if the symbol ∮ stood for:

"Find the remainder after as many 6's as possible have been subtracted from the product of any two numbers of this set {0, 1, 2, 3, 4, 5}?

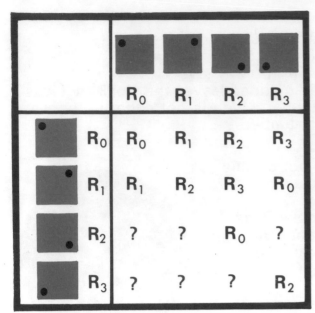

	R_0	R_1	R_2	R_3
R_0	R_0	R_1	R_2	R_3
R_1	R_1	R_2	R_3	R_0
R_2	?	?	R_0	?
R_3	?	?	?	R_2

Tables showing the symmetries of regular shapes can also be made.

Here is a simple one showing how any two rotations can be written as one rotation.

Complete the table.

Is it possible to use the pipe cleaner clock face described on page 93 to help you?

Look at the table for the 0, 1, 2, 3 clock face and compare it with the table of rotations of the square.

The square has eight different positions so it is possible to draw up a much bigger table of movements showing how any two of the eight movements can be combined and shown as one movement.

Study and discuss this table and then complete it.

	R_0	R_1	R_2	R_3	$\overline{T}$	$-T$	$\grave{T}$	$\acute{T}$
R_0	R_0		R_2			$-T$		
R_1	R_1							
R_2			R_0					
R_3	R_3							
$\overline{T}$					R_0			
$-T$								
$\grave{T}$				$\overline{T}$				
$\acute{T}$	$\acute{T}$							

94

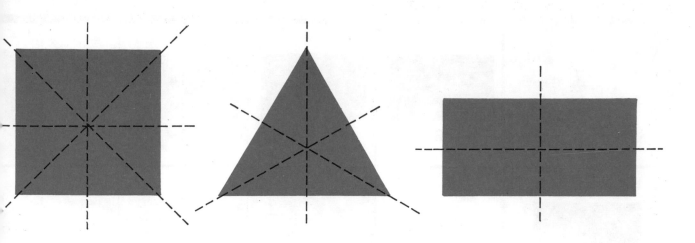

Examine these diagrams. What do they show?
What is the order of rotational symmetry for each of them?

How many lines or axes of symmetry has each shape?
How many times can each shape be "fitted into itself"?

Copy and then complete the following tables after discussing
them with your teacher.

$\oint$	R_0	R_1	R_2	T	T	T
R_0						
R_1						
R_2						
T						
T						
T						

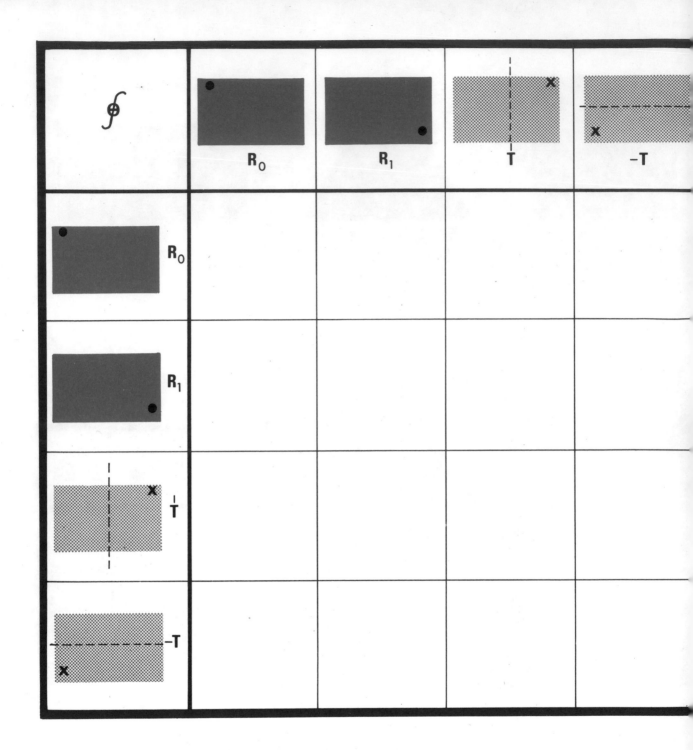